HEART DANCING

HEART DANCING

A STORY ALCHEMY
ADVENTURE

BY

KATHRYN ERIKSEN

Heart Dancing

A Story Alchemy Adventure

Copyright 2014 by Kathryn Eriksen. © All Rights Reserved.
www.KathrynEriksen.com

Infinite Joy Publishing, P. O. Box 57973, Murray, Utah 84157
Illustration by Joan Perrin-Falquet copyright 2014

ISBN 978-0-9908497-2-8
Printed in the United States of America
First Edition

Dedication

This book is dedicated to those stubborn souls who are courageous enough

to seek and accept the truth...

to become that truth in thought, word and deed...

to dance with love,

and live from their hearts.

Remember, your Divine nature is constant and changeless.

You can never destroy or harm it.

You can only ignore it.

Stop ignoring who you are and start living your life.

One heart dance step at a time.

Table of Contents

Acknowledgments

To take 100% credit for a book is not possible. I am so blessed to have many people in my life who have shared their hearts' message. If I do not acknowledge you by name, please know that your role in this book was still crucial to its birth.

You know who you are.

To my dear, faithful husband, you are my rock and my sounding board. The one person who knows me inside and out and who has helped me grow into the person I am today. I love you deeply and for always. My heart has always been yours.

To my wonderful daughter, your joy and light always amaze me. From the time I first held you in my arms, you taught me how to love. Your Divine essence is very much a part of this story.

I cannot fully express my deep gratitude to my wonderful parents, who encouraged, guided and loved me fully and completely. You were the first example in my life of unconditional love. You are even now dancing together, hearts joined and connected by love.

My brothers have to be mentioned here. I forgive you for all the times you teased me unmercifully, tickled me until I cried and pestered your only sister. You were just being brothers and that was how you communicated your love. It made me who I am today, so thank you.

To my twin, you are the mirror in which I see myself. The contrast between us is stark on the surface, but underneath, you and I share a strong bond of love. Thank you for showing me myself.

And finally, to the Divine Creator, the Source of love and light. Thank you for revealing yourself in each soul who enters this world. The fact that you gave us a small drop of your creative powers is mind blowing, unbelievable and empowering. All of my creations I return to you, to be enfolded in your infinite embrace. I love you!

Introduction

Have you ever watched a magic trick, either in person or on television, and wondered, "How in the world did they do that?"

A good magician acknowledges the mystery but may let you peek behind the curtain to show you how he drew the rabbit out of the hat. A great magician only sees the mystery that he has learned to manipulate at will. A smile and a nod acknowledge the accolades that come his way. A knowing that anyone can do what he just did, if only they look and *see*.

The mystery provides its own curtain of distraction, redirecting the audience from the truth. The real trick is to learn how to look through the mystery and discover the laws that created it.

On one level, the magician and the physical laws that he uses so adeptly are almost like a dance, coordinated, graceful and fluid. Moving together seamlessly so the impossible seems to occur. Turning and dipping to their own music, creating artful lines of motion and energy.

Life is that way.

We get distracted by the sleights of hand, the seemingly uncontrollable events that appear in our world as if by magic. If the events and circumstances that flow from them are judged as negative, then it can almost seem as if someone else is pulling our strings, while we jump in a puppet dance of helplessness.

It doesn't have to be that way. You are not the puppet on a string, at the mercy of some condemning all-present being...unless you think you are.

And therein lies the secret to everything.

You are what you think and believe. Whether consciously or subconsciously, your thoughts become the things of your life. When your thoughts are charged with emotional energy and action is taken, they come into physical form. Seemingly by magic, unless you understand the simple laws that govern their existence.

Why haven't you been told this simple Universal Law before now? Perhaps you were not ready to hear it. Or you were too distracted by the bells and whistles of living in time and space. You may have already heard about *thoughts become things* and tried it yourself, but when the results did not flow as quickly as you hoped, you gave up on the idea as being "crazy."

It's not any crazier than the shackled lady who disappears from the magician's stage. Except for one major difference.

When you know where to look, it all makes sense.

And that, dear reader, is the purpose of this book. To show you where to look in your own life to shift from victim to creator. To demonstrate how powerful you really are in the creation of your reality, your life and your dreams. To prove, once and for all, that the choice you face in each moment is between love and fear...and whatever you choose, that creates your next moment.

Embedded in the following story are clues to how we create our "reality." I also describe a 4 Step process that takes the stories you have created about past events and transforms them from lead to gold. Known as "Story Alchemy," the process is used throughout this book as a discovery and teaching tool. Additional information is available through my website.

As you uncover the limiting stories that hold you back and replace them with empowering messages of love and worthiness, your heart opens to its full capacity. Life (and love) begin to flow. Self-created obstacles or judgments disappear as you step into your own place of peace, love and joy.

And your heart begins to dance.

But who are you dancing with? Great question and one that only you can ultimately answer for yourself. As for me, I believe that we are here to express God in as many ways as possible. (Feel free to refer to an omniscient being as the Sacred Source, the Divine, the Universe; please feel free to substitute your own word whenever I use or refer to God)(Fair warning: I use the word "God" a lot!)

The critical ingredient is that you are never without a dance partner. Love flows around you, in and through you, but you have to open your heart (and your awareness) to it. Stay closed off, eyes shut tight and you will miss it, just like you missed the card being pulled from the magician's sleeve. Open yourself to these possibilities and you will discover a truth so simple yet so profound, that your life will tilt on its axis.

You are not alone in the Universe.

How can I make that statement without hesitation, doubt or fear? Because I have discovered it for myself. Through many hours of pain, frustration and even depression, I realized that I create my own misery. And that vortex of angst covered the treasure that waited for me, if only I was willing to pull back the curtain.

Your treasure is waiting...for you to step away from the quagmire of emotional distress and step into your greatness.

The concepts and ideas that are woven into the plot, characters and themes of Heart Dancing are my feeble understanding of threads pulled from many different sources. Some may read this book and think to themselves, "Why, this story is Christian – she hid that from me!" Others may be impressed with the diverse knowledge expressed by several of the teachers in the book. Still others may claim parts of the story as their own dogma. These different reactions only prove a major proposition in the book:

None of it is true unless you believe it to be true.

Heart Dancing is fictional and not based on any one particular religion or set of rules. Instead, it demonstrates (through the application of spiritual principles) that you create your life, in every moment and with each breath. You are the only one to make the decisions that become your reality. And you are the only one who can change it.

Heart Dancing is also not tied to any physical place or time. This book could just as easily have taken place near the ocean, or in a big city. The physical location is just the costume; the star of the show is you – as you magically transform your perspective to see from your heart...not your head.

And definitely not through the lens of stories that no longer serve you.

I am merely one person describing the process that has worked for me. My hope is that you will also find value in these techniques and concepts. My ardent desire is that you will realize that if you are not happy, the chains that bind you are self-imposed and you hold the key. My vision is that you will catch a glimpse of how your life will look once you accept your heart's invitation to dance.

Only you can decide to say "Yes" and take that first step.

Heart Dancing...it's the only way to live!

1

When the Music Stops

Music is the cup which holds the wine of silence.
~ Robert Fripp

The music that always danced in her mind's backdrop stopped abruptly as soon as she heard the words she had been secretly dreading for years. One minute it was playing as it always had, sad and sweet. It was the comforting background to her life. But as his words entered her awareness, her next breath sent the music to an unknown place, leaving her bereft and alone.

Would she ever find it again?

Christine stared at her husband while that one thought seared away any possible response she might have given him. It was the shock of the music leaving, without so much of an adieu or ciao. Christine and the music had been together for so long, ever since...No, she couldn't go there today. Not right now, when her life was falling apart in front of her eyes.

Her daughter, Savanna, was not so immobile at her father's announcement. Unlike her mother, Savanna had no idea this was coming. Teen age hormones do not make peaceful partners with strong emotions.

"What do you mean – 'you're leaving'?" Savanna asked, her voice rising to almost hysteria by the end of her question.

Brian Hartt stared at the floor as if it held the answers to life's questions. He heard the shock behind Savanna's question but knew that he could do nothing to ease this pain for her. Finally, with a sigh and squaring of his shoulders, he turned to look at his only daughter.

"Savanna, I know that this is hard for you to understand," he began gently, in the most caring, fatherly voice he possessed. "This has nothing to do with you..."

"How can you say that with a straight face?" Savanna looked to her mom for support but she only saw a woman whose dreaded moment had finally arrived. Christine sat in shock, still as a cold marble statute. No emotion, no reaction. Nada. Nothing.

That was the moment that Savanna stepped into the emotional void left by her mom, Christine. The rush of anger, hurt and rejection threatened to overwhelm her, but Savanna managed to spit out the three words that summed up her feelings at that moment. They were also the three words that no parent ever wants to hear from their only child.

"I HATE YOU!"

The words hung in the air, almost tangible because of the strong emotional charge. Her dad hung his head and avoided her eyes, his shoulders visibly shaking. But he gained control of himself and took a deep breath before he turned to his only daughter.

"Savanna, you have to give me some time to explain," he began gently, his voice shaking slightly.

Before he could continue, Savanna decided she had had enough of adults who were angry, bitter and confused. Her sky blue eyes turned dark as the storm clouds of her emotions threatened to overwhelm her. She glared at both of her parents, willing them to wake up from this nightmare and make up, but knowing that it was no use.

She stood up, pushed back her chair, and accidentally knocked over her glass of orange juice. Her mom's eyes snapped to the spill of liquid that was slowly moving to the table's edge, but she did nothing to stop the inevitable. Exactly like the drama that had just played out in their family.

Drip, drip, drip.

Savanna left them with their mess, grabbed her backpack, lunch box and helmet and slammed the door after her.

The sound was deafening in more ways than one.

Quickly pulling her bicycle out of the garage, Savanna's anger kept spiraling upward. The only solution was to get away from the source of her rage as quickly as possible. As she headed toward the safe and familiar haven of school, her legs drove up and down, trying to keep up with her thoughts. Her mountain bike shook from the vibration of speed building up through its tires. Her body shook as the air came in and out of her lungs, hard and fast, in time with the pumping of her legs.

Her only escape was to get to school as quickly as her fourteen-year old body and her two-year old bike would take her.

Her mind raced as fast as the wheels spun on the pavement. Instead of moving forward like her bike, her thoughts kept returning to the ugly scene that had just played out at breakfast.

When her dad announced he was leaving.

Not on a business trip. Not for a meeting. But leaving...forever.

Savanna kept hearing the defeat in her dad's voice when he said, "Christine, I can't take this anymore. I'm leaving." Her initial reaction of shock quickly turned to rage, and now she was still simmering in those turbulent waters. She knew that her parents were having their problems. Heck, anyone within a one block radius of their house would know that. But she never thought, in a million, trillion years, that her dad would just...quit.

How could her father just calmly announce that he was leaving? Give up? Did he no longer want them as his family? Another thought pounced on her wounded heart and would not let go.

Was she the reason why her father no longer wanted to be with them?

The power of fear behind that question clouded her mind and sharpened her attitude like a knife against a grindstone. It was no wonder that her day at school did not go well. She forgot to turn in a homework assignment in English, her math grade was not her usual A, and Jack, the bully of the class, decided to pick on her.

Wrong choice. For both of them.

After the scuffle, Savanna was left with bruises on her arms and legs, and Jack with a sore nose. Savanna sat outside the Principal's office lonely, sad and lost. If dejection and rejection could have a face, it would have been Savanna's at that moment.

"Why is all of this stuff happening to me?" she moaned to herself.

Just then, her best friend Mia sat down quietly next to her.

"Are you O.K.?" Mia whispered softly, her doe-brown eyes scanning Savanna for physical damage. Unfortunately, Mia could only guess at the extent of the internal damage that Savanna was heaping upon herself.

Savanna just shook her head and continued to stare at the floor. Her slim shoulders were slumped forward, as if to protect her heart. Her hands hung like limp rags between her outstretched legs.

"I can't talk about it now, O.K.?" she mumbled more to herself than to Mia.

Mia heard the intent behind the words and quietly hugged Savanna to show her support. She knew about the rough time that Savanna was going through with her parents. Mia's house had always provided a safe refuge for Savanna on the worst days.

Today, something had changed. Savanna was defeated and seemed to have given up hope. Although Mia's parents had never divorced, she had plenty of friends who suffered the agony of two sets of parents, two homes and two lives. She was determined to be there for Savanna, no matter what.

Janet Andersen, the Principal of the school, enforced a tough policy against fighting, especially if it involved physical contact. Both girls sat together, one in total defeat, and the other trying to show her love and support. The minutes dragged by like a slug slowly climbing up a tree, leaving behind a slimy trail of grief and pain.

Ms. Andersen's door clicked opened and Jack and his mom slowly walked out. Jack rubbed his nose and shot a look of pure hatred at Savanna, but she was still looking at the floor with the same dejected look of defeat. Mia poked Savanna in the ribs to tell her it was time to stand up. Savanna slowly got to her feet, head hung low.

Principal Andersen sighed when she saw Savanna waiting for her, and she motioned for Savanna to step inside. Mia smiled encouragement to her friend and waved a small good-bye. She motioned for Savanna to call her later and left.

"Is my mom coming?" Savanna asked with a tinge of fear in her voice.

Ms. Andersen took a moment to look at Savanna closely, and then motioned for her to sit on the sofa that was placed underneath the window. She had never been to the Principal's Office before, but everyone in school knew the drill. Wherever Ms. Andersen told you to sit in her office defined your punishment. Savanna breathed a sigh of relief – the sofa meant that she was not going to be suspended.

After they had settled, Ms. Andersen said, "Savanna, I know you have been going through a tough time lately. I spoke to your mom just a few minutes ago."

Savanna started crying into her hands. "I just don't know what to do," she wailed as if her heart was breaking.

Ms. Andersen waited patiently for the storm to pass, then handed Savanna the box of tissues that was always ready to serve. After Savanna had quieted, she said, "Watching your parents break up is one of the hardest things a child has to go through. But you will get through it."

Savanna shook her head, denying that she would ever be happy again.

"No I won't! My world is falling apart!" She cried in desperation, jumping out of her seat and turning to look out the window. Her slim frame shook like an aspen tree.

Ms. Andersen quickly rose and gathered Savanna into a warm hug. "God is here with you Savanna. He loves you so much, and he wants you to know that."

Savanna pushed away from her, instantly rejecting the words and the deeper intent of her statement.

"God doesn't love me." She turned her back on Ms. Andersen and looked out the window. "If he loved me, then why did he let this happen?"

Ms. Andersen looked with knowing eyes at her. She replied gently, "People have asked that question ever since they could form the words." She paused then continued, "I have always believed that your question is the wrong one to ask."

Savanna looked back at her principal in surprise. "What do you mean?"

Ms. Andersen just shook her head and said, "Just know that God loves you and wants to help you. What you need to do is get out of the way."

Savanna sat silently, looking at the floor and going over what Ms. Andersen had just said. It still made no sense. An overwhelming feeling of being lost threatened to engulf her again, but she took a deep breath and asked, "May I go now, please?"

"Yes. I know Jack provoked you, just like he does every day of the week. Next time, don't respond and you will be fine." Ms. Andersen smiled at Savanna and held out her hand. Savanna gave a small smile, took her hand and squeezed it to show that she understood.

"Thank you, Ms. Andersen," Savanna said softly as she grabbed her backpack and turned to go. The dejected set of her shoulders was like a neon arrow pointing to a young woman whose world was falling apart.

"Whenever you need to talk, I am here," the older woman reminded Savanna. The door closed softly as Ms. Andersen said a silent prayer for Savanna and her family.

Savanna's ride home was much slower and took a great deal longer than earlier that morning. The thought of entering the front door of her house and not seeing her dad waiting for her was a stone that hung around her heart.

Reality was a bit too harsh at the moment.

She decided to take a detour and stop by her favorite wooded park and watch the ducks in the pond. The golden aspen leaves had started to deteriorate and many had fallen to the ground, covering it in a blanket of yellow. The crisp air caressed her cheeks and reminded her that changes were coming, in nature and in her personal life. She found her favorite grove of aspens and parked her bike.

As Savanna sat under the golden canopy of the stately white trees and listened to the wind whisper through their leaves, she thought about what Ms. Andersen had said. Her mind kept repeating the words, "It's the wrong question to ask."

"What did she mean by that?" Savanna quietly asked, the ducks swimming placidly in the water.

The ducks ignored her and continued to search for bugs underneath the surface. She knew that they were just resting before continuing on their migration to warmer climates. Savanna sighed deeply and felt herself relax since the nightmare had begun this morning. Her mind wandered back to happier times.

"But Daddy," she cried in her high-pitched, five-year-old voice. "The ducks will starve if we don't come here every day to feed them!"

Her father, the center of her small universe, laughed and gave her a quick hug. "Honey, don't you know that God looks out after all his creatures, even these ducks?"

She looked deep into his eyes and nodded. "So I just need to ask God to take care of them and they will be O.K.? they will be fine?" She asked somewhat hesitantly.

"You got it!" He said as he grabbed her under her arms and spun her around so that her legs were parallel with the ground. After he set her down and her head had stopped spinning, her dad winked. "Race you to the car," he cried, already taking two steps away from her. She squealed in delight and ran as fast as her chubby legs would go. The world was a magical place and she was the Fairy Princess.

Savanna sighed deeply from the memory of that day and wondered aloud where the magic of her childhood had gone. The ducks continued with foraging, completely unaware of her anguish and pain. Savanna shook her head at their silence and started to gather her things. Just then, a flash of movement caught her attention.

"What the..." she cried in alarm. Savanna tried to hide behind the slender trunks of several aspens, not knowing exactly what she had just seen. Or why she was so startled. Her heart raced at the thought of danger and she made herself as small as possible.

When Savanna finally got the nerve to peek around the tree, no one was there. The sun was about to set and she knew that she should get home before her mom worried about her. But she had to find out what she had just seen. Or thought she saw.

Savanna quickly put on her backpack, got on her bike and rode to the other side of the pond. The heavy forest seemed to hold its breath as she scanned for any movement. When she finally turned back to start for home, the path stretched in front of her, up a hill.

And there, at the top of the rise, was the silhouette of a young woman and her dog, walking calmly into the sunset. They glowed with light and almost seemed to step off the earth.

Savanna stared, mouth open in astonishment. She froze, disbelief written all over her face. She finally sprang into action and rode her bike as fast as she could up the hill, but the woman and her dog kept walking farther and farther away. Savanna knew that she was riding hard, because her heart pumped and her breathing sounded like a freight train. The wind blew through her light brown hair with the fierce speed of a hunter on the scent of its prey.

But no matter how hard she tried, she could not catch up.

At last, Savanna stopped trying. She knew instinctively that the flash of movement she had seen out of the corner of her eye was this person and her dog. She also knew that they were both unusual.

Almost like they were from another world.

Savanna shook her head and turned towards home. Back to her own painful world.

Life had changed drastically in the Hartt household. When Savanna tentatively opened the back door after putting away her bike, she saw her mom, Christine, sitting at the kitchen table looking blankly out the window. She was still, a statue frozen in time – almost as if she had never moved away from that ugly scene that had taken place in the same space earlier that morning. And in many ways, on many levels, that was a fair assessment of Christine Hartt.

Savanna hesitated, but the creak of the door hinge gave her away.

"Come inside, young lady," her mom said in a deadened tone.

Savanna knew from years of experience that she should not challenge her mother when she was in this kind of mood. She moved obediently into the kitchen, not sure what to expect from the dark cloud that seemed to surround her mother. The back of her chair provided an anchor for her suddenly damp hands as she waited for her punishment.

It never came.

After several minutes of silence punctuated by a neighbor's barking dog, Savanna asked quietly, "Mom, are you O.K.?"

Her mother never turned toward her. Her profile was defined by the last rays of sunlight filtering past the trees and into the room. Her eyes were opened but unfocused, never once blinking. Her body was present but her mind and spirit seemed like they were on a different planet.

Savanna began to take in the state of the kitchen. The breakfast dishes were still on the table, eggs crusted over and droplets of butter curled around the crusts of toast long gone stale. The under counter lights were still on, a slight buzz in the air. The jar of honey was still on the counter near the sink, droplets liquefied on the side as if time had stopped. Normally, the kitchen would have been meticulously cleaned, straightened and set up for dinner. The table would be set for three and delicious smells would deliver an irresistible invitation to the family meal.

But not today. Her father was not coming back. And by the looks of things, her mom had checked out to another world. That left Savanna to fend for herself. By herself.

Savanna tried again to reach her mother, who seemed too far away to even care if Savanna stayed with her.

After a few more moments of silence, Savanna grabbed her backpack and slipped out of the room.

The atmosphere at home was so much darker than her wildest imagining about the punishment she would receive for fighting. All Savanna wanted to do was escape to the sanctuary of her room.

As she climbed the stairs, she wondered if her life would ever be the same again.

2

A Blessing in the Pain

*Music washes away from the soul
the dust of everyday life. ~ Berthold Auerbach*

Her mom never came into her room to say goodnight, even though it was a ritual they had followed faithfully since she was a toddler learning to sleep in her own bed. And her dad...

It broke her heart to think about her dad. He was her hero, her knight in shining armor, the one who could do no wrong. And now...he left them to fend for themselves. Savanna thought she knew what a broken heart felt like, but crying over a boy was nothing compared to your dad leaving.

That night, she could never find the cooler side of her pillow. Thoughts of anger mixed with despair and worry, keeping her mind agitated, energized and obsessed with learning the secret her parents refused to share. If only she understood what caused her gentle father to leave them, it might help ease her pain.

Sleep finally found her just before dawn. As the morning rays broke over the horizon and the songbirds broke out in their own liquid melodies, Savanna groaned. Her dream beckoned her to return to its warm embrace. She stretched and rolled over, closing her eyes when she suddenly remembered what today was.

Her first major Social Studies test.

The thought of not being prepared sent a slice of fear straight through her stomach. Savanna's feet hit the floor and she was ready for school in a nanosecond. If only she could slip out of the house without her mom hearing her, she could study a little bit before school.

As she gently padded down the curved staircase, backpack slung over her shoulder and her shoes in her hands, she heard a door open behind her. Savanna froze on the step, hoping that she was far enough down so her mom would not see her.

No such luck.

Christine was groggily walking towards Savanna's room when she spotted Savanna standing still. Their eyes locked and Savanna immediately became defensive.

"I have to go Mom," she declared defiantly, started back down the stairs.

"You wait just a minute, young lady," her mother cried in her authoritative voice.

Before she could round the stairs, Savanna had hit the first floor and was out the door, saying over her shoulder, "See you after school."

Christine's left hand gripped the railing, knuckles white from the tension that ran through her body. Tears threatened again as she realized that she may be losing her daughter as well as her husband.

She slowly sunk down to the landing, her back resting against the railing and her knees drawn tightly to her chest. She gave in to the strong emotions and let them wash over her like a tidal wave. Gut-wrenching sobs filled the house with pain and sorrow, a vortex of feelings that threatened to take her under.

Just as the pain seemed unbearable, a slender, furry body rubbed against her. The contact with another living creature who still loved her was an instant balm to her wounded spirit. She picked up the tortoise shell cat and held her on her lap, her knees finally released from the fetal position.

"Oh Bandelier, my life is falling apart," she murmured to the cat, who was purring and kneading her stomach.

Christine continued stroking the animal, grateful that something had brought her back from the edge of despair.

"I have to get hold of myself," she commanded. Even to her own ears, it sounded weak and pathetic, but it was enough to get her moving. The storm had passed, leaving her exhausted but somehow cleansed. As she gathered herself to stand, Bandelier bolted off her lap and down the stairs.

"Well, at least someone still needs me," Christine ruefully smiled to herself, as she began her day.

Savanna's day went from panic to sheer terror. When she arrived at school, it was only to find that the doors were still locked. She tried to set up under a tree and study, but her mind would not cooperate. On top of that, her stomach kept reminding her that she had skipped breakfast. Instead of time slowing as she hoped, it seemed to speed up like a freight train, moving her quickly on the crest of her dread to the test she knew she was going to fail.

Now, she sat looking at her test paper, in the quiet classroom whose only sound was the scratching of pencils on paper as everyone else around her wrote down their answers. A sinking feeling erupted in the bottom of her stomach.

"Why is this happening to me?" she thought for the millionth time. Another thought crowded in behind the last one. "I am going to flunk!"

She desperately did not want to bring home a bad grade. Her mom did not need that, on top of everything else that was going on in their house right now. But Savanna knew she was not ready to take this test.

Savanna glanced around at her classmates. They were all working intently on their tests, arms used to cover their answers.

Except for Meredith.

Savanna did not particularly like or dislike Meredith. She was the smartest kid in the class and she knew it. She was too serious for Savanna, but Savanna did appreciate the fact that she sat right next to Meredith in Social Studies.

Especially today.

Savanna's heart quickened with excitement. She knew all it would take was a quick glance at Meredith's paper to get most of the answers to the test. Savanna glanced up to see where Ms. Shepard was sitting at the front of the room. Her teacher was looking through other papers and was not watching the class.

It was now or never.

Savanna shifted in her seat and then casually let her eyes stray over to Meredith's test paper. She started copying down the answers and she had just begun to relax, when she felt a hand on her shoulder.

Savanna looked up in surprise. It was Ms. Shepard!

The normally porcelain-white skin of Savanna's face turned beet red. When she felt herself flush, her hands flew up to her face to hide the telltale sign of guilt. But she was too late.

Ms. Shepard told her to rise and led her out of the classroom to Principal Andersen's office. Every person in the class knew what had just happened. Savanna's head hung down in shame, and she dragged her feet as slowly as possible.

But the worst was just to come. When Ms. Andersen saw Savanna and heard Ms. Shepard's brief explanation, her normally kind eyes turned dark and angry. She pointed to the chair in front of her desk and Savanna sat down heavily, waiting for the impending storm that only took a nanosecond to erupt.

"Savanna Hartt, I am disappointed in you!" Ms. Andersen said in a firm voice. "What in the world were you thinking?"

Savanna just shook her head and looked at the floor as if her life depended on it. She asked softly, "Am I going to be suspended?"

Ms. Andersen walked over to the window. She shook her head in frustration and turned back to the distraught girl waiting to hear her fate.

"What do you have to say for yourself?" Ms. Andersen finally asked, breaking the silence.

"I am so sorry, Ms. Andersen." Savanna blue eyes darkened with tears. "I have never cheated before. It's just that I didn't study last night and when I saw Meredith's paper right in front of me, I couldn't help myself." Savanna paused as a new thought hit her. "This is all Meredith's fault!" she cried triumphantly.

Ms. Andersen held up her hand to stop that train of thought from going any further in Savanna's brain. "Don't you start looking to blame this on your classmate," she said sternly. "No one forced you to look at her paper and no one helped you copy down the answers."

Savanna put her face in her hands and her shoulders started shaking. The question that continued to plague her every waking thought popped out of her mouth.

"Why is this happening to me?" she moaned softly.

Ms. Andersen sadly shook her head. She walked around the side of the desk and sat in the chair next to Savanna. She waited for Savanna to finish crying and then handed her a tissue.

"Didn't we just go through this same discussion yesterday?" Ms. Andersen asked in a gentle voice.

Savanna nodded miserably, a glimpse of a smile playing at the corners of her mouth. Ms. Andersen caught it and patted Savanna's back.

"It's going to be alright," she said in an encouraging voice.

"What is my punishment?" Savanna asked bravely.

Ms. Andersen stood up and slowly walked back around the desk. She sat down and looked up something on her computer, then finally turned to the dejected young woman who waited for another piece of her world to fall apart.

"I can't waive the school's policy on cheating. You are suspended for two days, starting now." Ms. Andersen paused, her eyes looking intently at Savanna.

As Savanna stood up to go, Ms. Andersen said, "Wait a minute – I am not finished!"

Savanna's surprised look made Ms. Andersen smile.

"You will have to take the test over," she continued. "And you have to write a note of apology to Ms. Shepard and to each of your classmates. Each note has to be different and directed only to that person. No copying from one note to the next. And I want to see all of the notes at 10:00 o'clock sharp Monday before you hand them out."

Savanna mouth dropped open in astonishment. "But there are more than 20 kids in my class!" She cried. "It will take me forever!"

"And it will give you time to think about what you did and the effect your actions had on your classmates. Your teacher and each one of your classmates deserve a sincere apology from you. Please write each note in your own handwriting. No computers and no typing."

Savanna started to protest further, but the look on Ms. Andersen's face stopped her. She knew when she was beaten, and she slowly gave a nod of acknowledgement.

"When are you going to call my mom?" Savanna asked quietly, defeat leaving her body limp.

Ms. Andersen pulled the telephone closer to her and started pressing the numbers for Ms. Hartt's work. Christine worked as a nurse at the local hospital and was sometimes hard to reach. After speaking to several different people, Christine finally came on the line. They spoke quietly for several minutes and after the call was over, Ms. Andersen stood up and asked Savanna to wait outside for her mom.

As Savanna started to open the office door, Ms. Andersen called softly, "Wait."

Savanna turned around, hoping against hope that somehow a miracle had occurred and her punishment would disappear. No such luck.

Ms. Andersen walked around her desk until she stood in front of her young student. She smiled and said encouragingly, "I know you are going through a painful time, but there is a blessing to be found."

Savanna's disappointment in the absence of a reprieve made her response sharper than she intended. "I can't see any blessings and I doubt if I ever will," she said peevishly.

Ms. Andersen knew that Savanna was probably not ready to hear her next words, but she took a chance and shared it anyway. "You are responsible for your actions and your reactions, Savanna. No one else is." She paused for a moment and looked deeply into Savanna's confused eyes. "Think about that as you write your apology notes."

Savanna shook her head, amazed at the ability of adults to always find a moment to spring a lecture on a poor, unsuspecting teenager. She turned away from the advice and walked defeated towards the hallway. Savanna knew that the punishment she had just received from the school principal was nothing compared to what her mom was going to do to her.

If the wait yesterday felt long, now it was pure torture. Every sound or footstep made Savanna jump. Pulling her fingernails out one by one would have been more preferable than sitting on that hard bench, waiting to see the disappointment in her mother's eyes.

Savanna closed her eyes and leaned her head back against the wall. Her life had just spun out of control and she had no idea how to reset her personal orbit back to normal. Images flashed through her mind's eye of her future life as a criminal, sneaking around and stealing. Sordid pictures of life in jail raced through her brain. Savanna wondered what jail food tasted like. Vivid images of rats and weevils crawling in her food in the flour made her shiver with disgust.

"I guess that is all I am good for," she sighed to herself.

"What are you talking about young lady?" Christine Hartt stood over her daughter and she had obviously heard that last comment.

Savanna jumped in surprise and could only stare blankly at her mother. Two pairs of eyes that were so alike in physical appearance locked onto each other. After a beat of silence bursting with unsaid words, her mom told her sternly, "Wait here."

It was only a few moments before her mom and Ms. Andersen came out of the office together. They smiled warmly at each other and each gave a quick hug of support. Both women turned toward Savanna at the same time, with two different expressions. Expectation radiated from Ms. Andersen's eyes, while disappointment raged in her mom's eyes and the stern set of her mouth. Savanna slowly stood up and waited for her mom's cue.

Christine thanked Ms. Andersen and then led Savanna out of the building to the parking lot where her car was parked.

"Wait, Mom!" Savanna cried. "My bike is still here!"

"Go get it and put it in the trunk," her mom ordered.

The ride home was quiet. Savanna stared out the window and wondered how much worse her life could become. She knew her mom did not tolerate cheating and she expected the worst punishment ever. No television. No phone. No computer. No life. "Might as well be in jail," Savanna moaned to herself.

When they pulled up to their house, her mom turned off the car and sat, waiting for an explanation. Savanna started to open her door, but her mom stopped her.

"Well, young lady," she asked in her authoritative voice.

"I had a big Social Studies test today that I didn't study for," Savanna began weaving her story in the hopes that her punishment would lessen.

"I realized I was going to flunk the test, when Meredith practically put her test paper in front of me." Savanna glanced over at her mother to gauge the effect of her story. "I copied the answers so I wouldn't bring home a bad grade." She finished, a tinge of triumph in her voice.

Christine Hartt stared at her daughter in astonishment. It took her a moment to unleash her anger, but once she started, the avalanche of emotion overtook them both.

"Savanna Anne Hartt – that is the biggest bunch of crap I have ever heard! Do you really think that I would approve of you cheating just to get a good grade?" Savanna started to answer but her mom cut her off. "And for you to cheat just because you had the opportunity is no excuse." Christine took a deep breath to regain control of her emotions. "I can't believe you did this to me, especially right now," she said almost to herself.

Savanna's sobs filled the car. She desperately wanted to flee, but knew that if she did, her punishment would be much worse. She sat encased in the prison of metal, her body shaking in misery.

"I'm sorry, Mom." Savanna cried desperately. "I feel like my world has fallen apart and I can't do anything to stop it!"

Christine's anger dissolved in the heat of her daughter's distress. She leaned over and gathered Savanna into her arms, and they both hugged each other tightly.

"It's going to be O.K., honey." Christine finally whispered. "Both your dad and I love you very much. We're the one having a problem, not you."

Savanna's nose dripped quickly, her face stained with tears. "Do you happen to have a Kleenex?" she asked softly.

Christine smiled at her daughter and said, "That's my girl. Let's go inside and make some hot chocolate and talk."

Savanna nodded and a wisp of a smile crossed her swollen eyes. "I love you, Mom."

"I love you too."

3

Talk to God – He Just Might Answer

God whispers to us in our pleasures, speaks to us in our conscience, but shouts in our pains:
It is His megaphone to rouse a deaf world. ~ C.S. Lewis

Savanna felt better after she and her mom talked. They never touched on their current painful situation, but instead shared stories and laughed about small, inconsequential things. Although the house felt different because Brian was not there, the talk after school helped them both reconnect. The two women regained a shared vision of what their life would feel like, given this new and drastic change.

Savanna had to clean the entire house and write her apology notes that night. Teen Nickelodeon would be without her for two weeks, but all in all, Savanna thought that her punishment was fair.

She stayed home from school the next two days. Mia tried to visit, but her mom said that Savanna needed more time to think about what she did. Savanna spent a lot of time in her room, wondering about the direction of her life and how it could get so off course.

After dinner, her dad stopped by to see her, but he obviously did not want to stay. Savanna begged him to come up to her room so she could talk to him privately. He reluctantly agreed and slowly walked up the stairs.

After they both sat down on her bed, strained silence filled the void between them. After a few seconds of palpable tension, Savanna looked at her dad expectantly, with a touch of defiance in her eyes.

"What is going on with you, honey?" he asked cautiously. "You're not acting like yourself."

"Are you kidding me?" Defiance morphed into stunned stock. "Don't you know why I am upset?"

Her dad shook his head. "Yes, but I don't understand why you are acting this way," he said hesitantly, knowing that he probably should.

"It's you and Mom – nothing is the same since you left." Savanna's intense pain infused her voice with a somber tone. "I feel like someone has pulled the rug out from underneath me!" She sent a burning look of anger at her father.

"And I was the one to yank the rug?" He asked gently.

When she nodded, he studied her for a moment. "My relationship with your mother has nothing to do with you. The only way she and I can be happy right now is to live apart."

"Why can't you guys just get along?" Savanna cried in confusion. "You've been married for 16 years – haven't you figured out everything by now?"

Her dad looked at the carpet in reply. "There are some things that happened before you were born that we have never been able to resolve," he finally admitted softly.

Savanna was not surprised at this statement. She always knew there was something or someone who had caused her parents a lot of pain. She had never pushed the issue before, because both her mom and dad were quite adept at changing the subject and distracting her from pursuing that topic.

Now things were different. Savanna was determined to learn what it was that stood between her parents, especially since they both seemed to have given up on their marriage and their family. She could not imagine a future life without her dad by her side, encouraging her and supporting her growth.

It was impossible to consider and, up until three days ago at breakfast, as improbable as the sun not rising in the morning.

"Maybe I can help!" Savanna cried desperately. "What have you kept hidden from me my whole life?"

Savanna's desperation turned to anger at the thought of not being included in a family secret. Her eyes turned the dark color of the ocean just before a hurricane. She unleashed her full arsenal of pure emotion directly on her father, but he did not budge.

"Your mother will have to tell you that story," he softly said as he took her slender hands in his own.

Savanna tried to pull away from him, but he held her hands more firmly. He looked his daughter straight in the eyes and a parental tone crept into his voice.

"Respect the fact that we have our own history. Things happened before you were even born." He paused for emphasis then added, "And we are the ones who have to deal with it, not you."

"Mom won't talk to me about it!" Savanna cried with all of the emotion of an ignored fourteen year old who was desperately trying to cope with her confusing life.

Her dad shook his head. "That has been our problem too, honey. She refuses to talk about it, but she is so racked with guilt about her decision..." He stopped abruptly, hoping that Savanna missed that last word.

"Decision?" Savanna asked in a tone that said she would not stop until he gave her more information. "What decision?"

Brian sighed and closed his eyes. "We were faced with an impossible situation and she made a decision that she thought would resolve it. Unfortunately, it only made it worse. The guilt she feels because of her choice has trapped her." He sighed again, even deeper and looked Savanna directly in the eyes. "And that is all I am going to say about it."

"How can guilt trap a person?"

He shook his head and smiled a bit at her persistence. "I appreciate your determination to help," he said trying to lighten the mood. "Remember - that's your best quality."

His attempt to divert her pain fell swiftly flat. Savanna's cry of frustration was almost unbearable. Liquid sorrow pooled in her eyes and the anguish of her family imploding was as readable as a billboard. As Savanna sank lower and lower into her deep well of misery, her sobs filled the small bedroom.

Her dad looked into her eyes as long as he could, but broke their powerful appeal just in time. He knew that he was a breath away from being snared in the net of her distress. Instead, he pulled her close and they hugged silently, comforting each other with wordless love. After a time, they pulled apart.

"I love you honey," he said quietly. "And I will always love your mother." He paused thoughtfully before continuing. "I just can't live with her encased in guilt. I'm suffocating and I can't live my life the way I want to. I finally realized that she is never going to change, so I had to make a change." Defeat deadened his voice but his eyes pleaded with hers to understand.

Savanna nodded but still could not speak. Her swollen eyes and drippy nose said it all. She stood up slowly and walked over to her desk for a tissue. After she composed herself, she returned to sit down beside her dad.

"Change is something that we don't want, but sometimes we can't stop it." Her dad spoke softly, silently willing her to accept his decision. "Trust in God first and you will find your strength and love," he added gently.

Anger propelled Savanna from the bed. As she stood with her hands on her hips, she said defiantly, "Why would God want this family to be split apart? I can't trust in God!" Her breathing came fast and hard. "If God loved us, none of this would have happened!" she declared.

Her dad shook his head but did not say anything. He looked at the floor as if it held all the secrets of the universe. His search for wise words of advice failed miserably and his silent plea for additional inspiration went unanswered. He slowly looked up at Savanna, a cry for understanding written in the sheen of tears that veiled his eyes.

All that Savanna knew was that her world had permanently shifted on its axis. In her mind, one-half of the source of her present turmoil sat next to her. She just could not give up her anger at him, not yet.

It still hurt too much.

"Right now, the best thing for your mother and me is to live apart. But that does not mean I have to be apart from you."

"What do you mean?" Savanna asked hesitantly.

"Well, I have been thinking about this for some time. You could start staying with me on the weekends." Her dad shot a glance in her direction to see how she would react to this new suggestion.

Savanna's shock showed on her face. "You really aren't coming back, are you?" She asked in a quiet voice, already knowing the answer but dreading it just the same. Her dad smiled sadly and shook his head. No answer was necessary. The truth stared them in the face and they both turned away.

She was the first to speak. "Maybe if I can get Mom to talk about it, she would be able to move past it." Savanna looked hopefully into his eyes.

"Honey, I have tried to get her to talk about it for 16 years. If I couldn't get through, I am not sure you could."

The first hint of a smile flashed across Savanna's innocent face. "You wanna bet?" She said in a teasing tone.

He shook his head sadly. "This is way too serious for a bet."

Savanna's flash of good humor disappeared as quickly as it came. Her straight hair fell over her face like a waterfall, hiding her despair.

"Savanna, I was angry at your mother for a long time, but then something changed." He paused and gently pulled back the curtain of hair to look into her eyes. "I realized that I had to turn the entire matter over to God and let my anger go."

"What happened?"

"I finally gave up my anger and frustration, and let God into the situation." His dark brown eyes looked deeply into her startled blue ones. "Because I let go of my anger and asked God to become part of the solution, I finally found peace." He paused then added softly, "And...I was able to forgive her."

Savanna could not help but ask the one question that had been burning in her brain during this entire conversation.

"What did she do to you that made you that angry?"

Her dad smiled slightly at her tenacity but said sadly, "In respect for your mother, she will have to tell you that story and explain her actions."

"Then why are you leaving us if you forgave her?" Her sincere confusion cloaked a child's desperate need for safety and security.

"I can't live like this." His statement hung heavy in the air. "Even though I forgave your mother, she has not forgiven herself." His gaze seemed far away as he added, "We are at two different places in our lives. Neither one of us can be happy by just "going along" and pretending everything is O.K." Her dad paused while he gathered his thoughts. "I want more than that from my marriage," he added softly, almost as an afterthought.

Savanna still did not understand the dynamic between these two people to whom she owed her entire life. Her mind swirled with all kinds of possibilities about what could be tearing them apart.

"What did she do – kill somebody?" Savanna said flippantly, as only a teenager could.

The shock on her father's face quickly changed to a stern expression, but Savanna caught enough of a glimpse to know that she was on the right track.

"Honey, I love your mother and if she wants me back, I will come running. She has to work this out for herself first. I have done all that I could to support her, but..." He paused and looked at her seriously. "No meddling into her private affairs, O.K.?"

Savanna nodded but a spring of hope has just appeared in her otherwise bleak inner landscape. She leaned against her dad as his arm moved protectively around her shoulders. Her head still fit in the nest of his shoulder and he gave her a tight squeeze. She rested there for a moment, gaining strength from his warmth and love.

"Why now?" Savanna asked in a small voice.

He shook his head and looked intently at the floor. A deep sigh signaled a decision. After several moments of deep thought, he admitted, more to himself than to his daughter, "I just can't take it anymore."

The honest admission hung in the air, crystalized in a moment of truth.

Savanna's protective armor fell away at her father's admission of weakness. Although she knew her parents loved her, she also knew there was always a dark cloud hanging over her mother. Apparently, her dad had lived in the orbit of that dark cloud during their entire marriage. He needed to break free in order to be happy. His decision to leave the family was starting to make sense.

"But how did that happen?" Savanna asked curiously. "Why not just stay here and work it out?" Another spring of hope blossomed in her young heart, desperately wanting to believe in fairy tale endings.

Her dad smiled and ignored her second question. With a lightened mood, he asked gently, "You know what I started doing that helped me a lot?"

She shook her head and warning thoughts of an impending lecture formed on the edge of her awareness. She pushed them away, wanting to give her dad the benefit of the doubt. A small smile invited him to continue.

"It finally hit me that I could never change your mother." He paused and then continued. "The only thing I had control of was my own reaction. So I decided to change it."

Savanna's eyes rounded in recognition. "That's just what Ms. Andersen told me!" she cried.

He nodded in recognition – of her school principal and the wisdom of the advice.

Savanna couldn't help herself when she added, "Do all adults give advice from the same manual?"

Laughter filled the room. He hugged her quickly and said in his special voice, teasing her just like when she was eight years old and was playing on his desire to give her the world.

"Don't you know that there is a book that only adults can read?"

She knew they were playing a game but she felt so much better that she decided to play her part. "Really?" she asked innocently, deliberately making her eyes go wide and innocent. Long eyelashes fluttering like butterfly wings added to the effect.

Her dad smiled and added "Absolutely! No kid can ever read from this book, because it is written in a secret language that only adults can understand."

Curious, Savanna couldn't help herself as she asked, "But what is it called?"

He grinned mischievously and explained, "It is called THE BOOK OF LECTURES and whenever a child is born, a copy is given to every parent. It acts like an instruction manual. Some take longer than others to finish it, but it contains every piece of advice that any parent has ever given their children."

"I always knew that there was something like that!" Savanna cried in a high pitched voice.

"Teenagers are especially vulnerable to the advice given from THE BOOK," her father added, a sly wink emphasizing his words.

"No joke," Savanna said, almost to herself. She thought for a moment and then a daunting thought hit her like a sledgehammer. "When I have kids, am I going to know the secret language?" Horrific images of giving bad advice to her future children blossomed in her imagination. She shuttered in disgust and vowed silently to never fall into that trap.

Her dad laughed and hugged her again. "Sorry to tell you, sweetheart, but you don't have a choice."

"Whaaattt?" she cried. "But you just told me that I have control of my reactions – why would I have to learn a new language if I don't want to?"

"You may have control over your reactions, but you don't have control over this," he said gravely. "It's something that every person receives the instant they become a parent. And THE BOOK helps them when they need to give advice to their children."

Savanna level of upset ratcheted up several more notches. "But I don't want to give my kids advice!" she cried.

"When you are a parent, your strongest desire is to make sure that your kids don't make the same mistakes that you did."

"So you give them bad advice?" Savanna's puzzled look said it all. She just didn't get it.

Brian started grinning as he answered, "Who says it's bad advice?"

Savanna was about to argue when he started cracking up. Savanna's hurt shone in her eyes, until he finally stopped laughing. Her body language was defensive and angry, arms crossed and rigid shoulders.

Her dad's grin said it all. "Gotcha!"

It took a moment to digest, but Savanna finally smiled. "Good one, Dad," she said with a grin.

They stood up together and hugged again. "It's going to be O.K. honey," he said into her hair.

She nodded and felt somehow that he was right. She took his larger hands in her own and smiled into his eyes. "Thanks for explaining."

He squeezed his love in return and paused to look out of the window. He reached over to turn on her bedside light and said lightly, "Look how dark it's gotten at only 6:30! Fall is definitely here."

She nodded and followed him to the door. Savanna felt better than she had in days and was almost eager to re-enter the world. They started down the stairs when a sudden thought hit her on the third step.

"Dad – wait!" she cried, exasperated excitement filling her words with energy.

He turned and looked over his shoulder, eyebrow raised in a question.

"You never told me what you started doing that helped you so much," she cried, a little too loudly. They both missed the quick movement of Christine at the bottom of the stairs, moving out of their view.

"Oh – that's right. You sidetracked me, young lady!" His brown eyes twinkled in mock accusation.

Savanna grinned. "You always said I was an expert at that," she reminded him.

"Well, you certainly haven't lost your touch!" he declared ruefully.

"So..." she prompted.

"What was the question again?" he asked absentmindedly.

Savanna's exasperation seeped into her response. She said slowly, as if talking to a five year old, "What...did...you...do...that...helped...you...so...much?"

He turned and continued walking down slowly the stairs. Savanna followed, becoming more peeved at each step. She was about to launch into a full teenager rant when he reached the first floor. She was about to join him but he stopped her on the last step. They were about at eye level to each other.

He motioned her to lean forward so he could whisper in her ear.

Christine, standing still around the corner out of sight, leaned forward as well, even though she knew that she would never be able to hear his response. She held her breath, hoping against hope that somehow she could benefit from his advice. Christine was desperate to find a way back into Brian's heart and she would do anything to get there...even eavesdropping.

Savanna also held her breath. What in the world could he tell her that would make such a difference in such an impossible situation?

The moment seemed suspended in time. She felt his breath on her right ear and she waited.

Finally, he whispered, "I started talking to God...and God answered."

Savanna pulled away in shock. "What do you mean?" she cried in disbelief.

He smiled and nodded. "Just what I said."

On the other side of the dining room wall, Christine almost gave away her frustration and her eavesdropping. She clenched her hands into fists to regain control and silently turned back toward the kitchen, not wanting them to know that she had been listening.

Savanna was more persistent. She grabbed her dad's arm and dragged him out the front door. It was not until they had moved away from the house that she demanded, "What do you mean, 'God answered?'"

Her dad shrugged, knowing that it was hard to believe. "One night, I had all that I could take. I was so unhappy and had nowhere else to turn. I just could not get through to your mother, and I finally gave up."

Savanna stood frozen, waiting for him to continue. She had tasted that kind of desperation just this week, and caught a glimpse of what her father must have been going through for years. He took a moment to compose himself and looked up at the dark sky that was just starting to twinkle with stars. After a moment, he continued.

"Finally, I was fed up. It was the middle of the night, the house was quiet, but I could not stop accusing God." He paused to gage her reaction. Her intent look of attention, illuminated by the soft light coming from the porch, was all the encouragement he needed to continue.

"I grabbed a notebook and started writing down all of my accusations. I was so angry that my pen tore through the paper several times." He paused as he remembered the night that changed his life. "After I was done, I set down the pen and fell back against the chair."

Savanna was so caught up in the story that she couldn't help asking, "So what happened next?"

His chocolate brown eyes bored into hers, willing her to hear him. He took her hands and squeezed once, very hard, to emphasize the importance of his next words.

"I heard God's voice answer me," he said.

Savanna stepped away in shock, looking at her dad as if aliens had suddenly taken control of his body.

He knew that would be her reaction but he was intent on making her understand. "Savanna, I know this all sounds crazy, but I know what I heard. It was God answering my questions."

Savanna shook her head in disgust. "How can that be?" she accused in a peevish voice.

"I don't claim to understand – all I know is that I actually had a conversation with God."

Sarcasm dripped from her next words. "Did you tape record this conversation?"

He smiled gently and said, "No, it was all in my head. But I did something almost as good."

She couldn't help herself by asking, "What?"

He pulled her into a last hug and tossed over his shoulder as he walked to his car, "I wrote it all down."

The idea of her dad having a conversation with God was too much for Savanna. She shrugged her shoulders at the absurdity of the concept and dismissed it immediately.

"When are you coming back?" she called.

"I'll send you a text. I love you honey!"

She blew him a kiss and turned back to the house, feeling lighter than she had in days. Her thoughts turned inward, and even though her eyes were open, she did not see the slight movement at the front window inside the house.

4

You Have to Lose Yourself to Find it

Music is the shorthand of emotion. ~ Leo Tolstoy

The next day was Saturday. Her two days of suspension were over, but she still felt like she was in prison. Savanna had to get outside – now. She could not stand sitting at the kitchen table in the deafening silence, waiting for her mom to speak. Savanna did not like running away, but she had to escape the prison that her home had become.

She got dressed quickly and ran downstairs. Her backpack was loaded with bananas, muffins and juice. Savanna was not sure how long she would be gone, but she hated getting hungry and not having food with her.

Savanna called to her mother, who was still sitting in the kitchen, that she was going to ride her bike to the park. Her mom hesitated before giving her permission. "But make sure you are back by 10:00 – we have to run some errands."

Christine shook her head as she watched her daughter ride off to freedom. She had given up any hope of feeling free ever since...

Try as she might, she could not help thinking about that fateful day when she made the irrevocable decision that changed the trajectory of her life. Only the force of her strong will kept her from remembering. Usually, when she allowed herself to go back to that time, the music would play louder in her mind, easing her pain and sorrow. But now that Brian had left them, she didn't even have the solace of that sad melody.

The music, her constant companion since her life tilted on its axis, had started playing in her head just after she confessed to Brian what she had done. The look of shock that morphed into utter and total disgust was enough to send Christine deep inside herself, hoping to withdraw from the pain searing through her heart. When she was at her lowest point with no hope left, the soft melody started playing in her head.

It was enough to pull her back from the brink of desolation and despair.

Christine always knew that she had made the right decision, but she could never figure out why she was so wracked with guilt. On the surface, her decision was completely logical and rational. She convinced herself (and tried to persuade Brian, but it never worked) that it was for the best. Stubborn to a fault, she was so immersed in her story that she was never going to let it go.

Over time, Brian seemed to adjust to the new Christine and they were able to patch together a pleasing life. The birth of Savanna had been a Godsend in more ways than one. But now it seemed as if the cycle of life had turned again, and Christine had to relive those horrible days when the music had not yet found her. She was forced to face it alone, without Brian and without the solace of the haunting melody that had been her companion for so many years.

What if the guilt was right and she had made a terrible mistake?

That thought flittered across her mind and she had nowhere to hide. Usually, at this point in her thinking, the music would play louder and soothe her fears away. She never faced that question head on, because she was terrified of the answer. Keeping the question and the answer hidden behind the music was the best solution. Except now there was no music.

Did she make a horrible mistake that she would pay for the rest of her life?

There was only silence within. Christine had stopped praying a long time ago, when it seemed that God no longer cared about her. How could a loving God have allowed that to happen to her and Brian? No answer was ever given to that question, so she turned off all communication to God directly. Instead, all these years, her thoughts were encased in the music, which gave her a respite from the anguish of her decision and a small modicum of peace.

Except now, there was no music.

The sun was just beginning to break free of the horizon. Songbirds were calling to each other, singing gloriously to praise the new day. Even though the trees had started to turn and a slight hint of winter's chill was palatable, life still pulsated in celebration all around her.

Christine wondered if she would ever feel normal again.

A few blocks away, her daughter wondered the exact same thing.

There was no particular destination that morning. What Savanna wanted she apparently could not get. Her parents were going to stay separated and apart. They thought Savanna would be the bridge between them. Little did they know that she could barely hold herself together, much less connect the two of them.

Savanna found herself stopped next to her favorite spot under the grove of aspen trees that overlooked the pond. She parked her bike and settled on the crunchy carpet of leaves, pulling food out of her backpack. The ache in her stomach eased with each bite, but the ache in her heart burned stronger than ever.

"I wish I could just turn back the clock and fix them," she thought to herself.

The fall air was still warm, but the tinge of winter's bite was lurked at the edges of the morning. Savanna closed her eyes and let her body relax, as she wondered again about what her dad had shared the night before.

"I have tried talking to God," she thought defiantly. "But God never bothered to answer me." The spiteful thought came and went almost immediately. It was too much to consider – that all she had to do was ask God about her problems and presto - she would have an answer! Not to her minister, or her teachers or parents, but to her... Savanna Hartt.

Personally and directly.

Savanna just could not wrap her mind around that possibility. So her thoughts shifted back to the one question she was not supposed to ask. Savanna knew that Ms. Andersen was only trying to help her, but she had inadvertently added to Savanna's confusion by her advice.

"If 'why did this happen to me' is the wrong question, what is the right question?" Savanna thought to herself.

"Don't ever ask why," a quiet voice inside her head exclaimed. "It will only lead to more 'whys.'"

"Why not?" Savanna asked with a mischievous smile playing on her lips, her eyes still closed.

"Oh, so you want to play word games, do you?" The voice answered with a hint of good humor.

Savanna felt herself drift off into a deep sleep. When she woke up, she was groggy and disoriented. She sat up slowly and looked around to get her bearings.

The sun had continued its upward path in the sky. Beams of light filtered through the trees, making dappled patterns of color on the ground. The air had warmed up and Savanna stood up to take off her jacket. When her left arm caught in the sleeve of her coat, she twisted around to get it off.

And that is when she saw her. Or rather...them.

The shadow woman stood on the other side of the pond, her back to Savanna. Her silhouette moved gracefully in flowing movements. She faced the sun and it looked almost like she was dancing with its sunrays of luminous light. The dog sat patiently under a tree, ears and nose perked toward her owner.

Savanna broke from her trance and sprang into action. She quietly gathered all of her things and got her bike ready to ride. She had to find this person, discover who she was and how she could simply disappear. Besides, it was a lot more fun to solve a mystery than to wallow in the depressing misery that was now her constant companion.

As Savanna started to ride around the pond, she glanced to make sure that the mysterious woman was still there. Savanna just caught a glimpse of the woman and dog's silhouettes. They were walking away!

"Darn it," Savanna cried in frustration. "Not again!"

She rode as fast as she could through the thick grass, but never could catch up to them. She even tried calling out to them, but they continued to walk away calmly, not breaking their stride. The pair seemed to be from another world, their calm demeanor belying the fact that they traveled over a lot of ground without effort.

Savanna did all she could to catch up to them, standing on her pedals to get the most speed out of her bike. The handlebars waived back and forth and she used them to push herself harder and faster. Once she reached the road, the tires on her bike hummed tightly on the asphalt. Her light brown hair streamed out behind her like a banner, declaring to the world that she was on a mission. Despite all of her efforts, the woman and her dog disappeared around the next turn in the road.

As she reached that turn, she focused her eyes as sharply as she could to spot them. A flash of movement further down on the right was like a flag waving her on.

"Got ya," she cried to herself, finding new energy to continue her pursuit. When she reached the spot where she saw the motion, she saw a small dirt road that lead into the forest. Without thinking, her bike plunged in the new direction.

Savanna was determined to catch them. But instead, she caught herself.

After several minutes riding alone on the deserted road, Savanna finally had to stop and catch her breath. She looked around her and realized with a start that she did not know where she was. In her focused determination to reach the woman, she had not paid attention to where she was riding.

And now she was lost.

"Don't panic," she told herself sternly. "Why didn't I bring my cell phone?" she moaned to herself.

The forest of ponderosa pines and groves of aspens that surrounded her did not answer. It was much darker on this road because the dense foliage blocked out the sun. Savanna was in the middle of a dirt road that twisted in front of her and behind her. She was surrounded by an impenetrable forest that seemed devoid of life – human life.

Her heart pounded in her ears. Her breathing quieted from her recent exertion, but now a new fear tickled her spine.

Where was she? And was she alone?

Savanna took a deep breath and moved her bike toward the trees, out of the way of any predator that might just happen upon her. Newridge was a small mountain town in Colorado, and it didn't take long to leave the safety of the community and find yourself in the wilderness. Bears were focused on gorging themselves before winter forced them into hibernation. Accidentally coming across a bear in the woods at this time of year was not how she wanted to be remembered.

Savanna was just about to turn around and retrace her route when her eyes spotted a mailbox partially covered by small saplings. She parked her bike, slipped out of her backpack and walked over to see if she recognized the name on the box.

As she got closer, she noticed that the mailbox was shaped like a small house, complete with a front porch, windows and doors. Savanna had never seen a mailbox like this and she studied it intently. Painted a sunny yellow, it was complete with a bright red door and blue front porch. There were even two tiny rocking chairs waiting on the porch! Savanna half expected small, magical fairies to hang out the windows, asking in high voices what she was doing in their front yard.

"I must be losing my mind," she muttered.

Just as she was about to turn away, she noticed the initials, "DWTD" painted next to the tiny front door. When she looked closer, she could just pick out the same initials on the roof. "What in the heck does that mean?" she wondered out loud.

She took a step back and studied the mailbox and where it stood in relation to the dirt road. Why would someone have a mailbox out in the middle of nowhere unless they lived here?

A small path, invisible from a distance but recognizable up close, lead further into the woods behind the mailbox. Savanna took several steps down it, and realized that it was actually a narrow driveway. Recent tire tracks confirmed her suspicion that a house must be hidden in the trees. Should she go ask the people for help, or try to find her way home by herself?

She walked several tentative steps further down the driveway and discovered that she could see a short distance before it made a right hand turn. Savanna just caught a glimpse of a large golden tail just as it disappeared around the corner, and she knew that her mystery woman and dog had walked up this drive.

Savanna hesitated – should she follow them or turn around and go back home? She was scared of getting in trouble, but the pull of solving the mystery was too strong.

With a shake of her head, she decided to go for it. Her life was such a mess anyway, what did it matter? Savanna was starting to get used to being alone, without all of her friends or electronic gadgets. She realized with a flash of insight that she could actually tolerate it.

Her mind started to shift back to her problems and emotions threatened to engulf her again. The threat of thinking about her parents was enough motivation to keep going and solve the mystery.

At the very least, she could pretend that nothing was wrong for a few moments.

As she walked further down the driveway, she began to feel different. Her senses told her that this place was special. It was almost like entering the vestibule of a church. The more steps she took into the interior, the stronger the sensation of holiness settled on her.

Suddenly, she entered another world.

Leafy limbs gracefully formed a lacy canopy over the dirt lane. Sunlight filtered through the trees in quiet grandeur, dappled rays of light sparkling down to the small driveway. It was barely wide enough for a car, and it looked too natural to be man-made. The liquid notes of a songbird filled the magical space with natural music.

Savanna took a deep breath of the sweet air and felt her entire body relax. She paused for a minute to admire the beauty of this forest, and her mind stopped its maddening dance of thoughts. She stood in the middle of the lane, face upturned, eyes closed and hands relaxed by her side. The small frown of worry that had taken up residence between her eyebrows fell away.

For the first time in as long as she could remember, peace invaded her soul.

Time stopped and her world no longer felt like it was spinning out of control. She heard the same quiet voice again inside of her, and the two words it spoke to her infused her with happiness and joy.

"Welcome home."

She smiled in gratitude and opened her arms wider, accepting her place in this new world. She did not think – she just reacted from her heart. Open and receptive, her heart stepped forward and seemed to grow and expand. Savanna began slowly twirling in a circle, eyes closed, arms outstretched, palms open and relaxed. She looked almost like a flower, eagerly waiting to receive the sun's nourishment.

A solitary beam of sunlight filtered through the dense foliage and landed directly on Savanna. She felt its warmth and stopped her twirling so she could absorb its heat and strength. White light glowed from inside her eyelids. As Savanna watched the light, it collapsed into a glowing ball of blue.

She had never felt so happy and peaceful.

Time and matter stood still. It seemed as if the earth paused for an eternal instant and held its breath waiting for Savanna to choose and accept the message of the blue light.

Savanna's body remained standing in the middle of the magical forest, but her spirit knew what to do. She knelt in homage and bowed her head.

As soon as her spirit acknowledged the blue light for what it was, Savanna felt such a rush of love pour over her that she gasped in awe at its magnificence. The strength and power of it stunned her so much that she inadvertently opened her eyes.

And broke the connection.

Savanna found herself back in the forest, back in herself, but she felt disoriented and confused. Her breathing quickened and adrenaline flooded her body. Savanna had no idea what had just happened to her, but she knew that she had had enough for one day.

She quickly walked down the driveway, back to the mailbox. She grabbed her bike and swiftly slipped her backpack over her shoulders. Turning around, she pedaled as fast as she could back to the main road. If Savanna had thought to catch a quick glance over her shoulder, she would have seen two pairs of bright eyes glowing with the same love-force that she had just experienced in the forest.

But Savanna missed the clue. All she wanted to do was to get away from this place as fast as possible. A quick left hand turn and soon she was back on a familiar road, heading toward home.

Only to wonder about the other world she had temporarily touched. What had just happened to her? She felt overwhelmed with frustration and confusion, but when she remembered the blue light and how she felt, a small smile came to her lips. She breathed in deeply as the wind picked up slightly.

The rhythmic motion of her legs pumping the pedals seemed to settle her. As the familiar sensations of riding her bike filtered to her body, she let her mind wander over what just happened.

Urgent questions raced across her mind. Was there another world that existed alongside this one? Did she just stumble onto to something that no one else knew anything about? Or was she just crazy?

5

Secrets Revealed

*Love is a lot like dancing...you just surrender
to the music. ~ Unknown*

Over the rest of that weekend, Savanna grew more and more quiet. She stayed in her room or spent time in her tree house, just listening to wind as it wove its way through the trees. The turmoil of the last few days was gone, and in its place there was a sense of being held safely and wrapped in love.

Her family problems did not loom quite as large on her personal horizon. Her anger over her parent's doomed relationship began to fade as a new realization grew inside of her.

"There is something bigger than me!" she exclaimed to herself more than once.

That awareness of a larger life force began to change her entire perspective. She had to integrate that new knowledge into her life, and it took some time to accomplish it.

Sunday night, before she had to return to school after leaving in such humiliation, Savanna did not feel upset or anxious. Instead, she sensed an inner calm that she trusted to protect her from the accusing looks and derisive comments of her classmates. Savanna decided right then and there to trust in the calm feeling and let events take their course.

Tomorrow had its problems. Her energy was focused on today's troubles.

Finally, she was ready to talk. What she wanted right now was some serious answers to some serious questions.

After a quiet dinner and helping her mom put the kitchen back in order, Savanna gently took her mother's hand and led her to the couch in the den. Her mom looked at her in surprise but obeyed as if she was a small child and Savanna was the parent.

"Mom," Savanna said in a serious tone. "I need to ask you some questions."

Her mother nodded, the knowledge that this day would come glistening in her eyes.

Savanna looked down at their clasped hands before continuing. "I have been only thinking about myself since Dad left," she began softly. "And I couldn't help but feel that somehow this was all my fault."

Christine Hartt shook her head vehemently in denial. "Oh honey, I knew that is what you were feeling, but it just is not true!" She squeezed her daughter's smaller hand to emphasize her point.

Savanna took a moment to look deeply into her mother's sky blue eyes, so much like her own. Small wrinkles that grew deeper every year were the bookends, while long lashes that rarely saw mascara framed the windows of her soul. Savanna recognized the love and acceptance that shone from her mother's eyes into her own, and she smiled. Without a word, they both fell into each other's arms and started crying together.

They cried for times lost and opportunities missed. They shared the deep sorrow of knowing that change was inevitable.

After a few moments, the tears slowed and Savanna pulled away from her mother's embrace. She rose gracefully and walked to the kitchen, bringing back a box of tissue.

Christine shook her head ruefully while she attempted to make herself more presentable. "I never thought in a million years that this would ever happen."

Savanna sat back down next to her and waited. She knew that her mother was going through a desperately hard time, and she wanted to provide whatever comfort and support she could. In her new awareness, Savanna instinctively saw the need to be a good listener.

Her mom talked about how she had met Brian in college and instantly knew that he was meant for her. She was first attracted to him because of his athletically clean looks – tall and lean, with even features and a great smile. His light brown eyes and dark blond hair didn't hurt either. But it was his sense of humor and depth of character that really hooked her into a serious relationship.

They dated for three years and got married almost as soon as she received her degree in nursing. Christine got a job working at the local hospital while Brian went to law school. They enjoyed each other, had the freedom and money to travel and then decided to have a baby.

Christine paused at this point in the story, knowing that her old pain over past events would probably overwhelm her. When she looked at her daughter and saw the maturity in her eyes, Christine made the choice to tell the entire story and be done with it. She sat up straighter on the couch, squared her shoulders against the pain and continued.

"After I found out that I was pregnant, we were so happy!" She exclaimed, remembering that time when all things seemed possible. "It was so exciting and fun, until..."

This was the part of the story that Savanna had never heard. She took her mother's hand and gently squeezed encouragement. Christine took another deep breath and continued.

"When it was time for the sonogram, your dad took off from work so he could be there. They rubbed that jelly all over my belly and then we waited for the image of our baby to show on the screen."

Christine looked into the past and continued. "The nurse was happy and we were joking about whether the baby was a boy or girl, when the nurse stopped moving the paddle over my abdomen."

Savanna squeezed her mom's hand again and waited. She now had a glimpse of what was coming and sent a silent prayer to the love-force for protection. For her mother and herself.

"The nurse's face went white! Brian and I looked at each other and we knew something was terribly wrong with our baby. I tried to ask her a question, but she said 'Excuse me,' and left the room." Christine was caught up in her past, and she whispered, almost as an afterthought, "Actually, the nurse ran as if demons were after her."

Christine started sobbing again and Savanna hugged her as best she could. The pain that racked her soul was palpable. After a few minutes, Christine straightened and blew her nose. The loud clearing of nasal passages was so unlike her usually well-mannered mother that Savanna could not help but laugh.

Christine looked up in surprise at her daughter. "How dare you laugh at me, young lady!" she cried in mock disdain. Savanna smiled into her mother's eyes and nodded for her to continue.

"The doctor came in and looked at the images on the screen. He was visibly taken aback but quickly regained control." Christine shook her head as she remembered that painful moment. "He said he needed to speak to us in his office about the baby and then he just left the room."

Savanna waited patiently for the remaining part of the story. She now could understand why her mother carried a cloud of sadness with her, even though Savanna never knew the cause. She sent another silent prayer that the healing process would begin in her mother's heart.

Christine sighed and went on. "As we sat in the doctor's office, we didn't have a clue what was wrong with the baby." She paused and then said softly, "When he told us the baby was severely deformed and would never live a normal life, I could not believe it."

The shock of this news showed clearly on Savanna's face. "What did you do?" she asked softly.

Christine shook her head in disgust. "I was so upset that our beautiful baby was going to enter this world without his arms or legs that I..."

Savanna instinctively knew that this moment was pivotal to her mother's healing. She let the love-force in and then asked the one question she knew would lead to what had torn her family apart.

"What did you do?"

The pain in Christine's eyes was stark in its depth and sheer power. She grabbed Savanna's hands and held on tight, willing her daughter to understand.

"I was so angry at God and at myself." She began. "I just could not understand why God would let this happen to us!" The force of Christine's emotional outburst was almost the same as when she declared those words so many years ago.

"What did you do?" Savanna asked again, this time with more urgency.

"I went to see a different doctor," she said almost to herself, sadness dripping slowly off every word.

Savanna was almost beside herself. She had to know the truth, even if she had to sit on top of her own mother until she finally spit it out. She knew that she was almost there, but a tiny voice inside her head made her hesitate.

Did she really want to know?

Savanna almost fell for the seductive message of ignorance. Before her experience in the woods, she would have gladly embraced the silken cocoon of unawareness, but now she realized that there was so much more to her life than she ever imagined. Savanna no longer wanted to play small just to keep other people happy, especially her parents. Maybe if she dared to break free, her mom would too.

In that decision, the course of her life changed forever.

Instead of demanding to know the truth, Savanna sat silently, steely determination shining from her blue-gray eyes. When Christine did not receive the barrage of questions that she expected, she slowly looked up at her daughter.

And saw a complete stranger.

Christine knew that she could not hide the truth about her actions any longer. Excuses flashed through her mind about protecting Savanna and keeping her safe, but they no longer held the same validity as when Savanna was younger. Now, instead of a child who was easily distracted, Christine recognized a mature young woman who was not leaving until she knew the facts.

"Mother," Savanna said slowly, authority dripping from every syllable. Resolve and determination dominated her expression. Her feet, planted firmly on the floor, provided a solid base and conveyed a strong message. She was not going anywhere until her mother confessed.

"What...did...you...do?"

The simple question hung in the air, distilling years of anguish, doubt and guilt into four simple words that would not be denied, diverted or ignored. The moment for truth had finally arrived.

Christine thought about dodging the question again, but she knew it would not work. Once Savanna set her mind on something, a freight train could not stop her.

Although it terrified her to finally say the words again, after having spoken them to Brian so many years ago, she knew that she had no choice.

"I..." A small sob escaped before she finished the rest of the sentence.

"I had...an abortion."

The words hung heavy in the air, sucking out all the energy in the room. Savanna mouth opened in the classic sign of a person who has just received shocking news. After several beats of time and two hard breaths, Savanna spoke, anger and rage shaking through her body. "How could you do that?" she accused.

Christine wrapped her arms protectively around herself, as if to find some comfort. "You look just like your father when he asked me the same thing."

"You mean you didn't tell him?" The accusation filled the charged atmosphere. Savanna was beside herself. She instantly lost the controlled determination she had so recently discovered as the rush of anger flooded through her.

The look of disgust that Savanna aimed directly at her mother hit home.

Christine accepted the judgment passed on her, but she still could not help defending herself. Defiance set a hard expression on her upturned face. It was a battle that she had fought many times with her soon-to-be ex-husband. It always left her feeling utterly lost and alone, totally misunderstood and completely condemned.

"No one understands my pain! All they think about is the baby. He would have lived a horrible life – I saved him from that!" At this pronouncement, Christine fell against the cushions while deep heart wrenching sobs racked her body.

Savanna stood over her mother for a moment, loathing and rage battling for supremacy in her eyes. She waited until her mother's crying had slowed, and then she declared with all the raw emotions of a devastated fourteen-year-old, "I will never forgive you for this!"

Christine jerked like she was hit by a fist, instead of by words of judgment. The pain went much deeper than if her body had been physically assaulted.

"Now you know why your father left me, "she whispered almost to herself, disgust and defeat speaking volumes in the sag of her shoulders and downcast face.

Savanna could not stand being in the same room with her mother. She whirled around and fled up the stairs to her room. Her world had shifted once more, in a totally different and unexpected direction. The peace that she had found in the forest retreated to a small corner of her heart, while the rage she felt at her parents, especially her mother, took control.

She grabbed one of the pillows from her bed and began hitting it as hard as she could. Disgust, anger and hurt flooded her being, and the physical action was the only way to release those emotions before she was overwhelmed.

Savanna fell sobbing to her bed, her body racked with the knowledge that her mother was a murderer and her father could not stop her. Disillusionment and pain took up residence in her heart, as the emotional storm finally stopped.

The metallic residue of strong emotions still lay in her mouth, even though her eyes refused to produce any more tears. She was totally spent – physically, emotionally and spiritually.

Savanna rolled over on her back and stared at the ceiling. So many times, she had laid in this bed and look at the same ceiling, dreaming of her future. Memories of fairy-tale castles and princes when she was five were eventually replaced by horses and living with the Indians. Before all this trouble surfaced with her parents, her latest dream was to star in a movie. She pictured herself as the famous star, loved and adored by everyone.

Now, as she stared at that same ceiling, the only thing she saw was a sweet baby who never had a chance to live. Her mother was locked inside a prison of guilt and no one could reach her. And her dad, sad and lonely, had finally made the decision to break free.

Which left Savanna. Without choices or options.

"Why is this happening to me?" she moaned to herself, her misery and despair palpable presences.

Neither one had an answer.

6

Humble Pie

When the music changes, so does the dance.
~ African proverb

.

The next day, school waited for her. Instead of feeling dread, Savanna just felt numb. After the emotional turmoil of the weekend, the derisive looks sent her way by her classmates did not get a reaction. None of the comments penetrated her armor, and after a while, they became less strident and more muted.

Except for Mia.

In first period, Savanna's best friend glanced over at her every five minutes. She finally sent Savanna a note that said, "Are you O.K.?"

Savanna shook her head and stared blankly at her teacher. When class was over, Mia grabbed Savanna's arm and gently led her outside to the hallway.

"What is the matter with you?" she asked in concern.

"I can't talk about it." Savanna said dully. She turned to go toward her locker and Mia followed.

"Is it about the cheating?" Mia asked hesitantly.

Savanna let out a derisive laugh. "If only it was that simple."

They reached their lockers and started pulling out their next set of books. Several other students walked by and began whispering among themselves when they saw Savanna. She ignored them and continued to stuff books into her backpack.

Mia's frustration at her friend grew exponentially at each evasive answer. She finally slammed her locker shut and glared at Savanna.

"When you are ready to tell me, I'll listen." She paused for the dramatic effect. "Right now, you're just feeling sorry for yourself!"

Savanna's eyes glimmered with unshed tears. "Mia, I would tell you if I could! But it is a private family matter." She turned away. "I just can't talk about it."

Mia did not like being shutout and reacted accordingly. "Fine. See ya." Her bright blond hair flipped over her shoulder in classic teen girl dismissal as she turned to go.

Savanna dreaded going to see Principal Andersen. Part of her punishment for cheating was to write personal notes of apology to the teacher and every student in her Social Studies class. Savanna had to turn the notes into Principal Andersen before 10:00 a.m., so she could review them to make sure they were sincere.

Slow, dragging steps took her down the long hall and the open door of the school's secretary, Ms. Connie, who was a fixture at Newridge High School. Every student who ever attended the school, their parents, and their older or younger siblings, became very familiar with Ms. Connie. Parents considered her an ally and the students thought of her as a loving aunt. Everyone respected Principal Andersen, but she was strict and had very high expectations of the students. Sometimes, those expectations proved too much for both the child and their parents. Ms. Connie was the school's buffer between expectations and disappointment.

Savanna gave a wretched smile to the woman she had known since she was five and still believed in fairy tales. She desperately wanted to stay strong, but the armor that protected her from her classmates fell away without hesitation. Liquid sadness pooled in her eyes and Ms. Connie reacted instantly.

Oh, you poor dear," she exclaimed as she came from around her desk and pulled Savanna into a motherly hug.

Savanna accepted the comforting contact gratefully, and relaxed for just a moment. She had no more tears left to shed, but any shred of love she could find was helpful.

The embrace ended when Ms. Connie gently pulled Savanna back slightly so she could look into Savanna's eyes. It was the look of a wounded animal, without understanding or knowledge of why her world was so painful, that made Ms. Connie grab Savanna again in another hug.

"It's going to be O.K. dear," she said softly in Savanna's ear.

The dam broke and Savanna started sobbing uncontrollably. Just then, the door to Principal Andersen's office opened. The look of concern that she sent to Ms. Connie instantly propelled both women into action. They gently steered Savanna into the privacy of the inner office.

The phone buzzed and Ms. Connie turned reluctantly back to her job. Janet Andersen closed the door and guided Savanna, who had regained some control over her emotions, to the sofa. Several minutes passed in silence, while Savanna blew her nose and looked out the window.

Finally, she whispered, "Is my life ever going to be the same?"

Ms. Andersen smiled slightly at the thought that Savanna's question had changed from her previous victim mindset to a more philosophical bent. Savanna caught the smile and thought her Principal was laughing at her.

Ms. Andersen quickly dispelled that notion. After she explained, she said gently, "Savanna, I know it is hard to believe, but you are going through this experience for a reason."

Savanna's reaction was classic teenager – instant indignation and anger.

"How can you say that?" she demanded. "My life was perfect before all of this happened, and now..." She could not bring herself to finish the sentence, because the thought of what her future might become was too frightening to consider.

"Trust me, dear," Ms. Andersen said gently. "I have known both of your parents a long time. They will work through this."

Savanna looked at Ms. Andersen in surprise. "Really? I didn't know that." Savanna was beginning to realize that a lot of things happened in her parents' lives, before they even became parents. It was a new idea for her, and she tucked it away to think about later.

It was the older woman's turn to look out the window. Her mind drifted back to that fateful day when Christine Hartt had first walked into her office.

"When you were just a baby, I was a marriage counselor," she began. "Your parents were one of my first clients."

Savanna's full attention was focused on this woman whom she thought she knew. Savanna had never even considered the possibility that Ms. Andersen had not always been the Principal of her school.

Another thought struck Savanna and it left her in shock. "Did they tell you about the baby?" she asked hesitantly. Her eyes were wide with fear at the thought that Ms. Andersen knew about the family's darkest secret all the time that Savanna went to school.

Ms. Andersen hesitated a moment and then asked, "Is that what you learned that made you so upset?"

All she could do was nod, because anguish clogged up like a ball in her throat.

A deep sigh escaped from Ms. Andersen. She turned away to compose herself and said with her back to Savanna, "Your parents were on the edge of a divorce. Before they continued down that road, they decided to try to reconcile their differences." She paused as she remembered that painful time. "I am so sorry, but I can't reveal what they told me in confidence."

Savanna had hoped for a glimmer of understanding or some bit of information that would help her in her present despair. Instead, she had come face to face with another dead end. She was quiet for a moment while she digested what Ms. Andersen had just revealed.

"So they tried to work this out before?"

The older woman nodded. "I can't tell you all of the details, but I will share this...your parents love each other very much. And they love you more than they can ever say."

Savanna nodded, but a horrible thought struck her like a ton of bricks. She gasped as she instantly knew the truth.

"They stayed together because of me, didn't they?"

Ms. Andersen turned away so Savanna could not see the pained look in her eyes. The question hung in the air like thick fog that distorts shapes and colors. Ms. Andersen's silence shouted her answer as loudly as if she had a bullhorn.

Suddenly her life made sense. Growing up, Savanna always knew that some dark, mysterious secret haunted her parents. They always grew quiet when a young couple walked by with pushing a baby in a stroller, or when they saw a toddler's broken steps as he walked towards his parents. She knew they loved her, but a deep sadness seem to shadow them, waiting to cast its shape on their happiness. She was apart and felt very much alone whenever the darkness entered their lives. Never in a million years could Savanna have ever imagined what could have caused her parents to change from happy to miserable in an instant.

Until now.

Ms. Andersen turned back towards her young student, compassion and love shining in her eyes. Savanna stood up and took a shaky breath, unsure what to do or how to be. She was enveloped in a caring and supportive hug, as Ms. Andersen whispered, "You are strong enough to get through this. God will not abandon you at your moment of greatest need."

A sarcastic response waited to trip out of her mouth, before Savanna remembered her recent encounter with the blue light in the forest. That feeling of total love and acceptance that she felt while standing in the blue light came back to her, but she pushed it away. Her emotions were raw and unprocessed and she needed time to digest everything that she had learned.

In respect for Ms. Andersen, she did not argue or criticize her statement about God's support. She just did what any self-respecting teenager would do under these circumstances – she tuned it out.

"Here are my apology notes," she said dully, wanting to get back on familiar ground. "I wrote a different note to everyone, including Ms. Shepard." Savanna suddenly remembered something, and started digging deeper in her backpack. She finally found a smaller, finer envelope. "I know you did not ask me to do this, but I felt that I owed you an apology too," shyly handing the delicate object to Ms. Andersen.

"Why, thank you dear," Ms. Andersen accepted the card and admired its beautiful color.

"I have to get to my next class," Savanna said. "Thank you again for your help," she added as she gathered her things and turned to go.

Ms. Andersen smiled and patted her arm. "Trust me when I tell you that everything happens for a reason – we just can't see it sometimes."

Savanna nodded and left the sanctuary of the inner office. Instinctively, she knew that Ms. Andersen was right about things happening for a reason, but her current circumstances were so painful it was hard to see any good coming out of it. Savanna felt trapped and so alone. She sighed as she trudged slowly down the deserted hallway to return to the great unknown.

Her life.

7

What Took You so Long?

Those who danced were thought to be quite insane by those who could not hear the music. ~ Angela Monet

The rest of the day did not go any better. Her math teacher yelled at her for daydreaming (as if). She was the last one picked in gym class for dodge ball, and she spilled ketchup all over her brand new shirt at lunch.

Social Studies was sheer torture. Ms. Shepard gave the stack of apology notes to Savanna as soon as she walked into class. "Hand these out please," she said sternly.

Savanna had to suffer the snickers, giggles and sheer meanness of her classmates while she handed out each personalized note. The worse by far was Mia. When Savanna saw Mia's name on the envelope, she cringed slightly, knowing that nothing compared to this moment.

Mia waited expectantly, a superior smile playing on her lips. Savanna glanced at her ex-best friend, hoping for a small bit of forgiveness. But none was forthcoming.

As soon as Savanna gave Mia the card, Mia picked it up with two fingers, as if it contained leprosy. She then "accidently" dropped it and stepped on it, leaving an ugly black mark from her shoe.

Savanna could only stare in sheer mortification as the rest of the class snickered. She thought of running away and never coming back, but something made her straighten her shoulders, take a deep breath and return quietly to her seat.

"I am living in hell!" she declared to herself more than once. As soon as the final bell rang, she escaped on her bike and rode as quickly as she could toward the only peaceful place she knew.

The park.

It had not changed, except more leaves had fallen. The ducks still swam lazily on the calm water of the pond, occasionally disappearing underneath the surface. The songbirds flitted through the trees and the smell of fall hung heavy in the still air.

The park had not changed. But Savanna had. Her pain and confusion seemed to color her world, where hope and love did not exist.

Savanna parked her bike under her favorite aspen grove and sat on the ground, hugging her knees tightly to her chest. A desperate stream of tears accompanied her motion of rocking back and forth. She was the epitome of misery.

Finally, the storm of emotion passed and despair filled her. "What did I do to deserve this?" Savanna wondered to the clouds passing on their merry way, oblivious to her pain.

A dog barked in the distance, on the other side of the pond. Savanna glanced up and saw them. Again.

She was not about to go on a wild chase trying to catch these two. It was like trying to catch a handful of fog. It just was not possible. Her previous attempts had failed twice, and Savanna knew that she had to try a new tactic.

She suddenly remembered what her grandfather used to say about how to catch a butterfly. Instead of chasing madly after it, the only way to catch it was to be still. Maybe that tactic would work with the shadow lady and her dog.

She breathed deeply and closed her eyes. She focused on the inside of her eyelids and tried to recapture the peaceful joy she felt in the forest. Her mind slowly shed its burdens and a tiny smile played around the corner of her lips. To anyone passing, Savanna looked like a calm statute, serene and in control.

After countless heartbeats, a mystical voice softly asked, "What took you so long?"

Savanna's eyes popped open in surprise. She did not know if the voice was inside of her head or someone had actually spoken to her. She slowly looked around and just as she was about to close her eyes again, the voice asked again, more urgently, "What took you so long?"

This time, Savanna was sure that the voice was coming from behind her. She slowly leaned over and looked around the tree trunk. She gasped when she saw them.

It was the mystery lady and her dog! And they were sitting right behind her, less than 10 feet away. The shock of seeing them up close was balanced by the sudden realization that she never heard them approach. Even though they had to walk through a blanket of fallen leaves.

Savanna jumped to her feet and began chattering excitedly about how many times she had tried to catch them. She failed to notice the small frown that creased the brow of the woman, or the slight look of disgust that flashed across her face.

The lady was probably in her mid-20's with medium blond hair and fair skin. She was dressed comfortably in simple cotton garments, with her hair pulled back from her oval face in a ponytail. Something about her face reminded Savanna of someone else she knew, but she quickly dismissed that thought. She had never seen this person before; she was certain. The lady's intense eyes finally caught Savanna's attention and brought her chattering to a stop.

Deep green tinged with a hint of amber, the woman's eyes had a distant look, as if she saw her life through a different lens. Although her eyes focused on Savanna, the woman seemed to listen to an inner voice before she said or did anything. A quiet calm sense of knowing flowed from her to Savanna, but Savanna was still so excited about finally meeting them that she missed it.

When the woman stood up gracefully, brushing off her pants, her dog obediently followed. Savanna remained frozen, not daring to breathe. She tried to communicate her longing with her eyes, and after several seconds of staring into the woman's eyes, she asked softly, "Please stay."

The woman sighed and sat back down on the ground covered with a soft blanket of fallen aspen leaves. Her body immediately adopted the basic yoga pose and she took a moment to center herself before speaking.

"Savanna, I ask you again, what took you so long?"

Savanna's mouth gaped open in surprise. She sank to the ground like a balloon that suddenly popped, and she sat there, limp and deflated.

"How do you know my name?" she asked, her voice still in shock.

The woman shook her head in amused amazement. "They all start out this way," she laughed to herself. She took a deep breath before she continued.

"I will answer your question if you answer mine."

"You sound just like the voice in my head!" Savanna cried in confusion.

The young woman sat like a female Buddha, a knowing smile playing on the edges of her lips. Her silence acknowledged the truth of Savanna's statement. She waited for that truth to filter through Savanna's shocked brain before continuing.

"You still have not agreed to my proposal."

Savanna shook her head to clear any confusion that still lingered and took the plunge into the unknown. She instinctively knew that this young woman held answers to the questions that tormented her relentlessly. Even though it was against every social code that she had ever learned,

Savanna jumped into the challenge with both feet. Or head first.

"O.K."

The lady smiled, as if she could observe the mental debate that had just transpired inside Savanna's head. "Good girl," she said softly.

Savanna nodded her head slightly at the praise. "You first."

The woman's eyes glowed from an inner source. "I know your name because you are a favored and well-loved child."

Surprise lit up Savanna's face. "Are you talking about my parents?"

"No."

Savanna frowned slightly. Her confusion made her blurt out, "Am I your child?" The look of sheer amazement produced an amazing reaction in the other woman.

Laughter spilled out of the woman's mouth, like water playing over the rocks in a gentle stream. "I am just a messenger and guide," she managed to say while catching her breath.

"Then who else are my parents?" Exasperation crept into Savanna's voice.

"Think about it." The lady's laughter had died down, but as she calmly looked into Savanna's eyes, silent messages were sent of the Father who loved her.

Understanding dawned. Savanna's eyes grew wide and her hand flew to her mouth, the picture of astonishment. "You mean..." was all she could get out.

The woman smiled tenderly and nodded. Silence settled over them as first Savanna's mind and then her heart accepted this wonderful message. Savanna drew her knees up to her chest and hugged herself, marveling, "I am favored and well-loved by God!"

The wonder of this news broke through all of Savanna's despair and depression about her parents. She felt something inside of her jump up and down in joyful recognition of this message. As Savanna watched her internal drama, she saw her spirit reach out and touch the same blue light that she had first seen in the forest. Joy flooded every cell of her body and her heart burst open.

Savanna jumped up and began to dance, trying to express all the joy and love she felt. The woman sat calmly watching, knowing that this experience would change Savanna's life forever. After a few minutes of celebration, Savanna came back to herself and slowly sat down.

"Who are you?" Savanna asked quietly, all social pretenses gone. The awe in her voice made the woman nod slightly in acknowledgment.

"Now that you know the truth, it's my turn." The woman smiled as she reminded Savanna that her end of the bargain was still unfinished.

Surprise raced across Savanna's glowing face. "Give me just a minute; I don't want to lose touch with..." Savanna was not able to finish because she felt too overwhelmed by her experience.

The woman nodded and sat patiently, waiting for Savanna to come out of her meditation and return to the world of form. When she saw signs of Savanna returning to the present moment, she said, "Now that you have experienced the connection, you can always get it again. All you have to do is ask."

"Really?"

The lady nodded. "Are you ready to come back?" She paused to make sure she had Savanna's full attention. "Answer my question, please."

Savanna had to think back for a moment to remember what the question was. She recognized that her life would forever more be divided into "before" and "after" this moment. The knowledge that she was a favored child and well-loved were messages she grew up with, heard from the pulpit at church every Sunday and read in her Bible. But she had never felt it at the core of her being. Savanna still felt disoriented and dazed. But now she knew it was true.

Finally, she remembered the question, "What took you so long?"

"I am not sure what you mean." The question was a ploy for more for time and they both knew it.

A look of frustration flashed over the woman's face. Another unconscious person. The world was full of people who lived their lives in a trance, completely oblivious to the wonder and love that surrounded them. She hoped that after Savanna experienced her own connection to Divine Love, she would give up her unconscious habits and become more attuned to the deeper undercurrents of life.

The woman took a deep breath and re-centered herself. She knew from experience that people still clung to their limited ways of being, even after glimpsing their true heritage. It was just a safety mechanism. She did the same thing during her journey, a fact that she sometimes forgot.

"I must be patient," the woman muttered to herself, as if she were reminding herself of instructions given to her by someone else.

The brief interlude gave Savanna a chance to collect her thoughts. She knew that something incredible had just happened to her, but she still could not see the ramifications in her life. As she gazed at the woman, Savanna realized that she did not even know her name.

The lady seemed to return to the present at Savanna's question. "My name is not important."

"But it helps me to know what to call you." Savanna knew she had gained a slight advantage and she was not going to lose it.

The woman sighed deeply and looked down at her dog. The golden retriever was resting quietly beside her, eyes closed and snoring slightly. Just as they both turned their attention to the golden mass of fur, all four legs started jerking and a series of small barks came from her mouth.

"He's dreaming." The lady explained, while she stroked the square head. "Probably catching a rabbit."

Savanna smiled at the thought. "What is his name?"

"You are persistent, aren't you?"

"My dad says it is my best and worst quality."

The woman smiled and nodded. "I would have to agree with him." She unfolded her legs and stretched them out in front of her. At the change in her body position, her dog woke up and stretched as well. A loud yawn escaped from the dog's mouth, which made them both laugh.

"My name is Avery, and this is Avatar."

Savanna smiled at Avery and said, a teasing quality in her voice, "Well, you already know my name!" They shared a laugh at the small joke.

"Savanna, I have to go now. Why don't you think about how to answer my question and we'll talk again." Avery was poised to leave and did not wait for Savanna's response.

Savanna jumped to her feet. "When can we meet again? I have so many questions for you!"

Avery and Avatar were already about 50 feet away. She called over her shoulder, "You know how to find me."

Savanna started running after them, but stopped short when she remembered that chasing them did no good. She pulled herself back and closed her eyes, deliberately slowing her breathing. She called to Avery in her mind, "Thank you!"

She felt rather than heard Avatar's joyful bark. She opened her eyes and saw the familiar silhouettes at the top of the hill. A hand raised in acknowledgment made Savanna smile.

She gathered her things and returned home, a different person in mind, body and spirit.

That night, Savanna lay in her bed staring at the silhouettes of tree branches dancing on her ceiling. The wind was alive outside, and it moaned and pushed against the house. The turmoil outside almost matched the velocity of her inner conflict.

Almost.

She tried to come to grips with her mother's decision that had finally torn apart their family. Savanna just could not bring herself to accept her mother's solitary action that ended her pregnancy. She now understood why her father had finally chosen to leave. Instead of being mad at her dad, she was furious with her mom. Her mind raced a million miles an hour with thoughts of anger, hurt and resentment.

Her mother was not the person Savanna thought she was. All of her life, Savanna looked up to her mother, admiring her. Christine Hartt was a nurse at the local hospital and she took care of everyone as if they were her own children. In the small town of Newridge, Christine was well known. If a neighbor was sick or had an accident, Christine was the first person to bring food over to the family. She was the poster child for caring, especially for animals. Christine had even received an award for being the most energetic volunteer at the local animal shelter!

Savanna had always wanted to grow up and be just like her mother, until now. The truth about her older brother did not gel with the public image her mother had created over the years. Savanna felt like she was living with an imposter – and it was her own mother.

"I can't believe this is happening to me," Savanna moaned into her pillow. She tried to ask for the connection to God that she had felt earlier that day, but it kept slipping out of her grasp. The harder she tried, the more frustrated she became.

Bridging the events in her life with the other-world experience in the park was going to be difficult. There was no obvious connection and it left Savanna feeling angry and exhausted trying to find it. Her thoughts kept going in circles, judgment and accusations flying around in her head, just like Harry Potter on his broom in a hard fought Quidditch match.

Only, the snitch kept eluding her.

She rolled on her side to look out her window. She sighed deeply and pulled her covers closer to her, hugging them for comfort. As she stared at the trees dancing in the wind, she heard Avery's voice inside of her head.

"What took you so long?"

Savanna smiled to herself and decided she would think about her mom later. She had a homework assignment to finish!

"What took me so long to do what?" She mused to herself. "What is she talking about?"

Her mind sped backwards through the day, looking for clues that might help answer the question. The first time she heard that question was when she was sitting next to the pond, eyes closed and mind still. "That must be where the answer is!" she thought to herself in excitement.

Savanna got out of bed and sat on the floor, her back resting against the foot of her bed. She assumed the same yoga pose she saw Avery take and closed her eyes. She took several deep breaths and felt her heart rate slow. Gradually, her mind slowed down and Savanna could feel a space open up inside of her.

"I am here," she said in her mind.

As Savanna continued to breathe deeply and slowly released her thoughts, she felt something else rise up inside of her. Vivid images flashed across her mind – she was flying high above the earth on the wings of an eagle; she was joyfully playing in the ocean with a pod of dolphins; she was in the middle of a pack of elephants, sharing their power and majesty. She was herself but not herself. Instead, she felt a part of each image, enmeshed and connected with the energy flowing through the moment.

"What did take me so long?" she asked herself in amusement.

Suddenly, the images changed and the blue orb of light appeared. Unimaginable waves of love washed over her. She was overwhelmed with the beauty and power of it, and her eyes flew open in shock.

Savanna was back in her room, sitting on the hard floor, leaning against her bed. She still did not understand this "connection" but she knew that it was important. Savanna shook her head and slowly stretched, got up and went to her bedside table. Her journal was inside the drawer and she pulled it out, turned on her light and began writing.

At the top of the page, she wrote, "What took me so long?" Underneath that title, she began jotting down the first things that came to her mind. "What took me so long to get where?" "Where am I supposed to be?" "Who has been waiting for me?" And the most perplexing question of all. "How did Avery know my name?"

Savanna had always looked to her journal as a way to sort out her thoughts and feelings. She had started writing in it at a very young age and the habit had served her well. She now had a stack of journals that were a window into her childhood. Over the years, her handwriting had changed from childish to graceful. All of the hurts, bumps and bruises, both monumental and tiny, from her childhood had been faithfully recorded. Usually, writing calmed her enough and allowed her the space to decide how she felt.

But not tonight.

No answer magically appeared through her musings. She just got more confused. Maybe she was still not asking the right questions. Perhaps there was a question behind the question that Avery asked her.

Just as she was about to give up, she remembered what her dad had told her right before he left the house yesterday. She still did not believe that if she asked God a question that it would be answered directly, but if her dad said that it worked, then maybe she should just try it.

She closed her eyes for a moment and breathed deeply again, centering her mind and releasing her critical thoughts about whether this exercise could ever work. When she felt open to any possibility, she sat very still, pen poised over new page in her journal.

Savanna wrote down four words that changed her life.

"Are you there God?"

Without effort or strain, she immediately heard a deep, soothing voice in her head that she instantly recognized, even though she had no memory of ever hearing it before this moment. The voice was calm and its deep, vibrant tones resonated throughout every cell in her body.

In fact, every cell in her body was dancing!

She seemed to be outside herself, looking at her body in amusement as it reacted to the voice. She could actually see the energy flowing freely in and around her physical self. And then she noticed the color of it --- the blue orb of light was now swirling around her...and through her!

The shock of seeing the blue orb flowing through her physical body was too much for Savanna's mind to comprehend. She felt the jolt of slowing down to her physical body and it saddened her to think she had to play small again.

Or did she?

That question hung in the air as she turned off the light and returned to bed. She curled up in bed, her mind reliving what had just happened. It was triggered by her writing down a simple question to God.

She received an answer - immediately, directly and intimately.

God was there instantly, as soon as she asked. Savanna hugged herself with the knowledge that she did not have to deal with her problems by herself. Another thought struck her like a jolt of electricity.

If God was on her side, then what did she have to worry about?

She felt herself open up to the possibility of living without fear or anxiety, no matter what happened to her. Her heart beat faster as she caught a brief glimpse of a life filled with absolute calm, total joy and all-embracing love. Heart dancing...but after several more beats, it became too much for her mind to comprehend.

It was just too much, too soon.

Having had two experiences of being outside her body in the same night was exhilarating. But it was also exhausting. Her world kept shifting on its axis until she did not know which way was up. She felt like she was doing somersaults under water and had lost the way back to the surface. But then she remembered the trick she always used to use to find her way back to oxygen.

"Just follow the bubbles," she smiled to herself.

Her last thought before she fell asleep was to wonder if the bubbles would be a vibrant, glowing blue.

8

Love Divine

Without music, life would be a mistake... I would only believe in a God who knew how to dance.
~ Friedrich Nietzsche

Savanna woke up on her bed, staring at the ceiling and wondering what happened to her. She felt disoriented and confused, but she was also happy. Deliriously happy.

She remembered finally meeting Avery and her dog, Avatar in the park and having a strange conversation with her. The events from yesterday and last night were fuzzy and slightly unreal.

Suddenly she sat up in bed as her memory latched onto the out-of-the-world events that happened last night, while she was alone in her room. Dancing with the blue orb – with dolphins and eagles. Feeling utterly and completely loved. She hugged her knees to her as she rocked back and forth.

How was all of that going to make sense as she started her day? And what about her mom? Just because Savanna felt totally loved, was she still supposed to forgive her mother for doing the unforgivable?

The pounding questions drove her out of bed and into the bathroom. She felt her joy slip away and become enveloped with more familiar emotions – anger and frustration at herself and her parents.

Savanna paused to look in the mirror.

Her eyes looked back at her, haunted and alone.

"No one loves me." The statement seemed to hang in the air, sucking the life right out of her. Her mirror image just stared back, waiting for a reply.

Savanna leaned closer to the glass to look into the depths of her own eyes. As she held her own gaze, her mind slowed its frantic race of thoughts and was finally still.

Silence. Inside and out.

Savanna's heart began beating faster, as if she knew that something big was about to happen. She could feel her lungs expand and contract with each breath, coming faster and faster through her nose. Her mouth was open in expectation and she could feel excitement welling up inside of her. She had no idea what was happening, but she instinctively knew to maintain eye contact with her mirror image.

Suddenly, Savanna saw it. Pure love and joy – radiating from inside her own eyes! She gasped and blinked involuntarily, not sure what she had just seen. But her spirit knew – it was dancing inside of her!

Thoughts flew across her mind as she tried to analyze what had just happened. She no longer felt that no one loved her. In fact, she knew just the opposite was true.

Love Divine.

That thought made her smile for the first time in days. She had actually seen Love Divine – staring back at her from the mirror!

Suddenly, she realized that she had to see Avery. Right now. She was the only person who would understand what had just happened.

Savanna looked at her Sponge Bob alarm clock and saw that it was still very early. The sun had not even begun to rise. She instinctively knew that Avery and Avatar went to the park in the early morning hours. Savanna calculated whether she had time to stop by the park on the way to school, and quickly decided to do just that.

She threw on some clothes, gathered her books and backpack, and rushed downstairs. Her mom was still sleeping, so Savanna left her a note that she had gone to school early and would see her this afternoon. She grabbed a muffin, an apple and a bottle of water, threw them in her backpack and quietly closed the door behind her.

As she was walking towards her bike, she realized that Avery and Avatar might need food too. She ran back inside the house, grabbed more food and left quickly.

When Savanna arrived at the park, she rode on the other side of the pond and headed toward the hill. The sun was just coming up over the horizon and the sky was about to dance with the light of a new day.

And then she saw them – two silhouettes moving together at the crest of the hill.

Savanna slowly walked up to a respectful distance and took a deep, cleansing breath. She closed her eyes and turned towards the sun, letting the warmth of the rays fill her being.

She felt at home.

After several moments of complete peace, Savanna opened her eyes and watched the dance Avery was performing to an unseen audience. She gracefully moved from one pose to another, flowing like the wind. As the sun rose, it created shadows behind her that seemed to dance too. It looked like Avery was dancing with the sun and her shadow at the same time!

Savanna sat down to wait, enjoying the show. Avatar walked over and lay down next to her, putting his head on her lap. Savanna smiled at the dog, happily accepting his gesture of friendship by scratching him behind the ears.

Finally, Avery stilled her movements, brought her hands together in the universal symbol of prayer, and then she did something totally unexpected.

She actually bowed to the sun!

Savanna smiled as Avery walked towards her. "That was beautiful!" She said softly, not wanting to ruin the magical moment. Savanna waited for Avery to sit on the other side of Avatar before she asked, "But what were you doing?"

Avery did not answer for a few moments. Her eyes followed the flight of the geese as they began their long trek south for the winter. She seemed to absorb her surroundings and meld with them, aware of every nuance and subtlety. Finally, she spoke.

"That was my heart dancing with love," she said reverently.

Savanna shook her head in amazement. "How can your heart dance with love?" she blurted out, a little too loudly.

Avery sighed softly, slightly exasperated. After a long moment that seemed to stretch into eternity, she asked her student quietly, with a tinge of frustration, "Savanna, how do you know that my heart *can't* dance with love?" She looked intently at her protégé and waited patiently.

Savanna sat up and pulled her legs close to her chest in a protective gesture. She started crying softly, rocking herself back and forth, closing in on herself Avatar whined and looked at his master for direction.

Avery slowly stood up and began picking up her things. Avatar jumped up and shook himself once, as if to say, "That didn't go well!"

Savanna remained locked in her misery. She knew that she had blown her chance with Avery and that thought made her even more miserable. She heard Avery and her dog get up and start to leave, but Savanna could not seem to break free of the vise-grip of self-pity that consumed her.

Avery paused just long enough to look down at Savanna. She knew that Savanna did not have the means yet to process this new way of spiritual living. She needed more time to learn how to live from her heart instead of from her head.

Before Avery turned away, she reached down and gently touched Savanna's shaking shoulder. Savanna did not acknowledge the contact but her sobbing stopped abruptly.

Avery leaned down and whispered softly, "You still have not answered my question."

Savanna looked up in surprise, her pale face a mottled red from her crying. "You mean I have another chance?" She managed to ask.

Avery sighed and placed her things down on the ground. She knelt in front of Savanna and looked her deeply in the eyes. Although no words were spoken, Savanna could feel the power of love and acceptance that poured forth. Savanna sat spell bound, not daring to breathe or blink, as she fell deeper into the world behind Avery's eyes.

The self-pity that had encased Savanna's heart cracked open, revealing her true self. No conscious thought disturbed the flow of love. For those precious moments, Savanna's mind was silent, allowing something else to emerge into her awareness. All she could do was wait for it to reveal itself. Although her emotions were also quiet, she knew that something momentous was about to happen.

It did not take long. Eternity seemed to hold its breath as Savanna recognized the truth shining from Avery's eyes. Soul met soul and the connection that was always there, but hidden behind the curtain of self-absorption, joyously stepped forth.

Love Divine.

Avatar watched silently, his liquid brown eyes focused on the two humans. His doggy grin said that he knew exactly what was happening. His tail swished back and forth slowly, content to mark the moment in time of a timeless transformation.

Finally, Avery broke the connection by blinking. She sat back on her haunches, and seemed to gather herself back into her body. Savanna fell back against the slender trunk of the aspen tree and took several moments to collect herself.

Avery stood up, gathered her things, and looked at Savanna with the patient love of a parent for a small child who was in desperate need of guidance.

"You are a spiritual being having a human experience."

Savanna was about to protest, but she stopped herself in time. She nodded instead and said "Thank you," in a small voice. Avery looked into her student's eyes to gauge whether Savanna was centered enough to go back into the world of physical form. After a few seconds, she nodded, and then she and Avatar were gone.

Savanna started cleaning away the signs of her distress. She enjoyed the muffin and apple and felt ready to face the day. She was still very confused by Avery and her vague comments, but she felt a trickle of hope inside. Savanna flashed back to seeing Love Divine in the mirror and suddenly she knew the answer to Avery's riddle, "What took you so long?"

Savanna jumped to her feet and raised her arms wide above her head. She released herself from the prison of self-pity. Joy radiated from her as she offered her answer.

"I had to wake up!"

Her loud voice startled the ducks and they quacked once, before flapping their wings in a desperate attempt to clear the pond before danger overtook them.

Love and joy spilled out of Savanna's heart. Words could not express the emotions she was feeling, so she did the only thing any self-respecting spiritual being would do.

She danced.

Without a care, without reservation, and without worry. The music was internal and the audience was unseen. In that moment of complete freedom, Savanna found her own heart connection.

Several miles away, deep grey eyes lit up and a smile played across Avery's face. She threw her head back and laughed at the sky. Her new student was not so unconscious after all.

9

Heart Vision and the "Real" World?

I see dance being used as communication between body and soul, to express what it too deep to find for words.
~Ruth St. Denis

Nothing was the same after that morning. Savanna was still angry and confused about her parents, but the intensity of her emotions paled in comparison to the glimpse of Divine love that she experienced. The petty annoyances at school that usually set Savanna's teeth grinding did nothing to ruin her good mood. She sailed through her classes, focused and alert. She even nailed the math pop quiz!

Savanna's entire perspective changed with the realization that she had to wake up to see her world in a new light. She looked with compassion at her classmates, seeing beyond the petty games they played so intently, to the spiritual person who was just underneath the surface. From this new heart perspective, Savanna remained apart from the emotional turmoil that usually embroiled her. Instead, she remained calm, centered and absorbed in the string of moments that connected her day.

Of course, the first thing that Savanna wanted to do was to share this new information with her best friend. She knew that she had hurt Mia's feelings by not sharing her pain and distress over her parent's separation. Mia's retaliation in Social Studies was just a way to show Savanna how much she had hurt her. Savanna could now see through the mean gesture of stepping on her apology note.

To make it right with Mia, a text apology would just not be enough.

Savanna waited until just before lunch before approaching her former best friend. She was standing with a group of other kids when Savanna came up behind her and gently touched Mia on the shoulder. The conversation that flowed between the teenagers stopped suddenly, almost as if a gunshot had exploded. Mia turned around quickly to see what had made her friends stop talking. A surprised look flashed across her face, before it was masked by a sheer disgust.

"Mia, I have to talk with you," Savanna said urgently, trying to get Mia to move away from the small group. She leaned in to whisper in Mia's ear, "Something incredible has happened to me – and you are the first person I want to tell!"

Savanna knew that Mia could not resist being the first to know about anything new. She counted on that to motivate Mia to move past her hurt feelings and become friends again. Unfortunately, Savanna miscalculated.

"I wouldn't be caught dead being your friend again," Mia declared, a little too loudly. The others snickered at the put down and started to drift away. Mia turned to join them when Savanna said urgently, "Mia – we have to talk!"

The plea of desperation hit Mia squarely in her heart. She was tired of being mad at Savanna and missed her company. Her desire to be friends conflicted with her need to let Savanna suffer just a little longer before they made up.

Savanna looked into her friend's eyes, willing the love force to connect them. Mia was oblivious and completely unaware of what Savanna was doing. Savanna laughed to herself and instantly thought of Avery's reaction to her unconscious questions. Mia caught the smile and instantly became annoyed. "Why are you staring at me?" she accused in an irritating voice.

Savanna threw up her hands in surrender and said quietly, "Just meet me at the fountain with your lunch so we can talk."

Mia's expression softened slightly at the mention of the fountain. It was the place where she and Savanna met as first graders, new to the school and eager to be friends. The small fountain anchored a slightly larger courtyard surrounded by tall trees and lined with stone walks. It was their magical place. They spent many moments of their childhood playing dolls, then horses, and more recently sharing secrets about the boys they liked.

Savanna did not even wait for agreement. She turned and walked toward the cafeteria line, fully expecting Mia to be at the fountain.

"I don't hang out with cheaters," Mia said loudly, looking around to make sure that others kids within earshot heard her.

Seven minutes later, Mia turned the corner with her lunch in hand, and came upon Savanna sitting on the wooden bench, face turned up towards the sun. A peaceful expression and her index fingers and thumbs touching in a circle made Mia instantly think of her mom's yoga teacher.

"Are you running away to be a Buddhist monk?" she asked Savanna derisively.

Savanna's eyes flew open. "You came!" she exclaimed, totally ignoring the snide comment.

It was Mia's turn to be caught off guard. "Did you really think I could be that mean?" she asked defensively.

The last thing Savanna wanted to do was to continue their argument. She smiled at her friend and relaxed, patting the empty space on the bench. "Let's eat and see if we can't get back to being friends." Savanna paused for dramatic effect. "I have so much to tell you!"

Mia grinned and sat down. Soon, they were comparing notes about school, their classmates and catching up on the miniscule details of each other's lives that only a best friend could appreciate. Mia waited until after all the food was eaten before venturing into more dangerous waters.

"Savanna, I have been so worried about you!" She said sincerely. "Those two days you were suspended were the longest in my life."

"I am so sorry that I did not share what was going on. Mia, you know that you are my best friend, right?"

Mia looked with concern into the troubled eyes of the person she considered her sister. "What do you need from me?" she asked gently.

Savanna smiled at the offer of friendship. She grabbed Mia in a hug and they rocked back and forth for a few moments. Finally, Savanna broke the embrace and sat up straighter, a joyful laugh escaping from her lips.

Mia became confused and defensive again. "What is it that has made you so happy?" She thought a minute and exclaimed, "I know – your parents are getting back together!"

Savanna shook her head sadly. "That's not going to happen anytime soon," she said sadly. "But I don't want to talk about my parents. I want to tell you what's happened to me!"

Mia decided that it was time for her to listen and not ask questions. She smiled her encouragement and waited for Savanna to continue. But she was not prepared for the words that tripped out of her friend's mouth, like the silver water that was flowing down the sides of the fountain.

"I started writing in my journal again...and I asked God a question." She paused and joy blossomed on her face. "And guess what? I actually got an answer!"

Mia's mouth fell open, and her eyes widened in shock. It only took about two seconds for her frozen expression to shift into a look of concern.

"What do you mean, 'you got an answer'?"

Savanna sighed and realized that she needed to start at the beginning. She told Mia about her trips to the park and spotting Avery and Avatar, but never being able to catch up with them until she was still. She tried to explain about her encounters with the blue orb of light, but by the time she reached that part of the story, Mia had had enough.

She stood up, agitated and frustrated, trying to come to grips with what her friend had told her. It was just too much – too foreign and too uncomfortable. Mia hardly ever thought about God or whether love surrounded her. She definitely did not believe that people and dogs could fly or disappear at will. Mia was more aware of the clothes that would make her eyes stand out or the appreciative looks that she received from some of the boys in her class. All of this talk of God made her shut down and refuse to consider whether Savanna's story was even true.

Instead of happiness and acceptance, Mia instantly erected a brick wall.

Savanna shook her head at the restrictions of trying to explain the unexplainable in words. "You have to experience it for yourself, Mia," was all she could say.

Mia shook her head. "I know you've been going through a hard time with your parents, but I don't get this spiritual stuff." She crossed her arms against the notion that she was really a spiritual being having a human experience.

The realization of what was missing hit Savanna in the face. "Mia, why don't you come with me tomorrow morning, and you can meet Avery yourself?" Eager to help her friend understand, Savanna was not prepared for utter and total rejection.

Mia shook her head. "Sounds too weird for me," she said as she stood up, picked up her things turned away in disgust.

Savanna's frustration quickly turned into anger. "You don't care about me!" She shouted at her friend's back, dropping her tray on the stone patio for emphasis. The glass of juice rattled against the plate and spaghetti sauce splattered all over the tray. Several drops even hit Savanna's shoes, which made her even angrier.

Mia flicked back her blond hair in the universal teenage gesture of dismissal. She kept walking away from Savanna and turned the corner, disappearing from sight.

The peace and joy that had radiated from her heart disappeared as quickly as her best friend. Savanna knew she had made a fundamental mistake during that entire exchange, but she could not figure out what she had done wrong. She sighed and began to clean up the mess she had made.

Just as Savanna was about to stand up, an authoritative voice above her asked, "Savanna Hartt, what are you doing here, all by yourself?"

Savanna recognized the stylish pumps that could only belong to Ms. Andersen, her principal. She smiled sadly to herself as she stood up to face her.

"Can I talk to you for a minute?" Savanna allowed her eyes show the depth of her emotion and Ms. Andersen instantly responded. They walked through the cafeteria and then onto the administrative offices.

Once they settled themselves on the sofa, Ms. Andersen asked quietly, "What is it, honey?"

Savanna threw up her hands. "I don't know where to start!" she cried in frustration.

Ms. Andersen sat quietly waiting. Silence rained down on them, while the afternoon sunbeams highlighted the dust particles floating lazily in the air. Savanna slumped over, her hands on her legs, the picture of total dejection and surrender.

Savanna felt a deep need to share everything that happened to her since the day that she got suspended. All of it. The part about chasing Avery and Avatar. Learning about what was really tearing apart her parents. Feeling lost and alone and seeing Love Divine in her own eyes.

After Mia's painful rejection, Savanna desperately needed some kind of validation that she was not crazy. Since this crisis first started, Ms. Andersen had been the calm, reassuring harbor where Savanna could drop anchor and just rest. But the compassionate woman had become more than that; she had also caused Savanna to think more deeply about her own reaction to the recent dramatic events in her life.

She finally sighed and began talking.

Once the words started, Savanna found that she could not stop. There was no censure or judgment over the content or the meaning of her words. Instead, the torrent of words just flowed out of her, as if a dam had broken inside. And in a way, it had.

"I am so confused!" She cried at the end of her monologue. "Why is this happening to me?" She moaned to herself, almost forgetting that Ms. Andersen was still in the room.

Ms. Andersen stepped into the silent gap that followed the question Savanna kept asking herself. "That is quite a story, young lady," she said with a bemused look in her eyes. "May I tell you a story that might help you put things in perspective?"

Savanna nodded miserably and slouched even lower in the cushions. She could not help thinking to herself, "Here comes another lecture."

Ms. Andersen seemed to read her mind. "I am not going to lecture you!" Exasperation filled her tone. "Why don't you wait and listen to what I have to say before you condemn or judge it?"

Savanna's cheeks turned red in embarrassment. "I'm so sorry, Ms. Andersen. I wasn't thinking." She risked a glance at her principal and saw only loving acceptance. Savanna relaxed and looked at Ms. Andersen, waiting for her to begin.

"Savanna, have you ever noticed that adults want to tell you what they have gone through, so you can avoid their mistakes?"

Savanna look of surprise was all the answer Ms. Andersen needed to continue.

"You know the reason for that, don't you?" she asked in a tone that said "well of course, everyone knows that."

Savanna shook her head in confusion and said the first thing that popped into her mind.

"Because it's their job?"

Rich laughter rang out in the office. Ms. Andersen shook her head and said, "Just listen to my story and then you will understand."

Ms. Andersen started again. "Life is like a huge painting – as big as anything you can imagine."

"Just like the Jumbotron at the new football stadium?" Savanna asked, her mouth turned upward slightly.

Ms. Andersen rolled her eyes to the ceiling, and then laughed.

"O.K. Think of life like a Jumbotron," she said grudgingly. After a moment, she continued.

"Everything that could ever happen to any of us is on that Jumbotron. All the ups and downs, the joy and pain, the losses and tragedies. The Jumbotron displays it all, in every detail." Ms. Andersen paused to see if Savanna was listening. Sky blue eyes stared intently at her, and it looked like Savanna was holding her breath.

"Breathe, dear." Ms. Andersen could not help but say to her young student. When she was sure that Savanna was not going to faint, she went back to her story.

"When we are born, we are all the same distance away from the Jumbotron. In fact, everyone has their nose pressed tightly against it." Ms. Andersen paused for emphasis. "How much of the entire screen could you see if your nose is smashed against it?"

"Not much," Savanna said with certainty.

"That's right, you won't see hardly any part of that giant screen. Just what's in front of your nose," Ms. Andersen nodded before continuing. "But you know what happens as time goes by and we get older?"

Savanna shook her head in dismay. "What?" she asked.

"As you get older and experience more about life, you take a step back from the screen. You might think of it as one step back for each year lived." Ms. Andersen paused to look at her young protégé. "Can you tell me how much you could see then?"

Savanna shrugged her shoulders. "It depends on how far back you are."

"Exactly!" Ms. Andersen shifted on the sofa, facing Savanna. "And who do you think can see more of the screen, a baby with its nose pressed against it, or a parent or teacher who has lived on this earth for many years?"

The silence between heartbeats was deafening. Savanna sat with a stunned expression on her face. "You mean my parents can see more of the screen than I can?"

Ms. Andersen nodded. "So don't judge them for their actions, when you can't see the same screen that they can."

Savanna thought about the meaning behind Ms. Andersen's story, and knew that it was a turning point for her. She had to figure out how to let go of her judgment of her mother's actions. She still wasn't sure how to do that, but she decided that she would give it some time. But her anxiety about how to treat her mother caused her to blurt out, "But what do I do now?"

Ms. Andersen took her smaller hands gently in her own. "Your parents have their own problems to solve. You can't be the one to solve it for them." She paused, and then added, "Keep telling them that you love them and forgive them. Tell them out loud and in your own mind."

"How can I send them love in my mind?" Savanna asked incredulously.

"Isn't that just what Avery sent to you?" Ms. Andersen asked gently.

Savanna stopped breathing for a moment. "You're right!" she cried excitedly. "She did send me thoughts of love – I just didn't tune into them!"

Ms. Andersen smiled knowingly, and added, "Since you have already experienced what it feels like to be the recipient of waves of love, don't you think your parents could use the same thing right now?"

"But I don't know how to send waves of love!" Instead, waves of frustration brought a sheen of tears to Savanna's eyes. "How can I send love when all I feel is anger and pain?" The question seemed ripped from her very core. Savanna's head dropped into her hands, as sobs racked her body.

Ms. Andersen wrapped her arms around Savanna tightly and rocked her like a baby. When the storm began to die down, she handed the box of tissues to Savanna and stood up to give her young student a private space to make herself presentable.

"I have one question to ask you," she said while looking fondly at Savanna.

Savanna dared to look up and saw only love shining down on her.

"Is this the most pain you have ever felt in your entire life?"

A shocked look stole over Savanna's upturned face. "Absolutely!" she cried with utter conviction.

Ms. Andersen nodded. "The depth of pain you experience is balanced by its emotional opposite." As she paused for effect, a cardinal chose that moment to sing its melody outside the window. They both glanced at the bird and paused to appreciate the golden notes that seemed to hang in the crisp fall air. The songbird's timing was perfect and the beautiful notes dripping from her small throat spoke of love and glorious beauty.

Savanna slowly turned away from the beautiful aria, back to her mentor. She raised her eyebrows, silently asking her to continue. Ms. Andersen smiled at her and shook her head.

"The opposite of pain for you is different than it is for me or anyone else. But you chose this experience so you would know your own capacity to feel both emotions."

Savanna was not sure what to do with that information. For her to choose this experience meant that on some level, she knew this was going to happen. Her mind could not wrap itself around that concept, but the thought triggered another idea that was almost too astonishing to believe.

"If I chose this experience, then does that mean that my parents chose their experience with the baby?" Her eyes were wide in shock as the implications of that question reverberated through her.

Ms. Andersen smiled fondly at her and said gently, "Don't get too balled up in the greater implications of what you are experiencing." She paused for effect. "It may be too much, too soon and it may throw you off what is really important."

Savanna nodded at the wisdom of her statement. But she still could not resist asking the obvious question.

"What is really important?"

Laughter filled the air as Ms. Andersen hugged her. "Oh my dear, you have to discover that for yourself."

Savanna knew it was time to go. She stood up slowly and walked the short distance to her principal. A deep breath steadied her and she nodded as a new thought crossed her mind.

"Thank you for telling me about the Jumbotron," Savanna said sincerely.

Ms. Andersen grabbed her in a fierce hug and said softly, "Someday you will pass on this same lesson to another person. You are creating your own heart dance." She paused as gratitude welled up inside of her. The merest whisper escaped. "I am honored to help you learn some of your first steps."

They pulled apart and smiled into each other eyes, love vibrating like a strand of connection between them.

"Thank you," Savanna said softly as she turned to go.

It was not until much later that night, while lying in bed and thinking about their conversation, that Savanna wondered why Ms. Andersen was not surprised or shocked about Avery and Avatar. Most adults would have focused on the fact that Savanna was meeting a stranger in the park, instead of offering helpful analogies for her family problems.

"I guess that's another mystery I will have to solve later." Savanna mused to herself as she drifted off to sleep.

Her mother was not so lucky.

After a tense dinner together, Christine and Savanna had drifted to their own corners of the house. A call down the hall to Savanna's room wishing her good night was the last contact that Christine had with her daughter. She knew that she had to give Savanna more time to accept the past, but the fear that kept bubbling up was whether she had also lost her only daughter, just as she apparently lost her husband.

Christine lay in her bed, wide awake and staring at the ceiling. Ever since she had confessed her deepest, darkest secret to Savanna, they had lived together in a tight truce. She knew that she had to give Savanna time to sort through what had happened, but as each day passed, Christine began to wonder if she would ever get her daughter back.

Savanna's reaction to the abortion was exactly the same as Brian's had been all of those years ago.

Horror.

Anger.

Judgment.

Disgust and loathing.

And finally, rejection.

Pretty much in that same order. It made Christine wonder for a nanosecond if she *had* made the right decision about the baby...

As soon as that thought crossed her mind, it was bludgeoned immediately by relentless arguments that supported her position.

The baby was better off not being born. What kind of life would he have had with no arms or legs? He wouldn't have lived that long anyway and she was saving him from suffering.

Usually, that train of thoughts would soothe her enough to believe that she was right and everyone else was wrong. Usually, the sad, haunting music would start playing inside her head and she would focus on it and let her internal conflict about her past go. But ever since Brian left her, the music stopped playing. And it forced her to look at her motivations more squarely than she had in a long time.

Tonight was much worse, because now Savanna also knew the truth and judged her just as harshly as Brian.

Feeling justified and victimized at the same time, tears welled up in her eyes and rolled down her face. If she was right about the baby, then why did she feel so bad? Especially when Brian had changed his position on the entire matter.

Several months ago, Brian brought up the baby again. She resisted and wanted to keep that topic buried under the placid surface of their life together. But he persisted and finally she had no choice but to hear him out.

It was the first warm day of the summer. The deck overlooking their backyard sparkled in the early morning sunlight, and the flowers she planted and placed in pots overflowed with color. After placing two cups of coffee and several muffins on the table between their two chairs, he gently led her outside.

She knew the moment had come when her actions would catch up to her. Numbness took over and she walked woodenly to her chair, sitting on the edge and waiting for his verdict.

It was not the one she expected.

Instead of harsh accusations and anger, Brian was calm and peaceful. He looked at her with deep love and compassion and simply said, "I forgive you."

Out of a million different scenarios that played out in her mind of what this scene would look like, it never occurred to her that he would grant her forgiveness. It was just not in the script! Her reaction to his three life-altering words was sharp, direct and cutting.

"What do you mean, 'You forgive me'?" A flood of anger swept through her body, propelling her out of the chair to stand over him.

"What gives you the right to forgive me?" Christine's words were clipped short by her emotion, her tone harsh and unbending.

Brian just shook his head. He refused to take the bait by answering her question. He was not affected in the least by her tirade and just sat with a knowing smile that drove her nearly crazy.

"I have been angry at you ever since it happened," he said softly. "But I reached a point when I didn't want to be angry anymore."

"So you forgave me?" Derision and sarcasm dripped from each word, turning each syllable to ice.

Brian did not react to her tone but maintained his placid demeanor. He picked up his coffee and settled back in his chair to enjoy the view of their expansive back yard.

Christine was livid! How dare he drop an announcement on her about "forgiveness" and then refuse to defend it? She began pacing back and forth, agitation and anger zeroing in on a target.

She finally stopped her pacing and stood in front of him, hands on her hips and defiance bleeding out of every cell of her being.

"What...gives...you...the...right...to...forgive...me?"

The words were spoken in soft voice, but each syllable was so filled with rage that an explosion appeared imminent.

Brian glanced up at her then returned his gaze to the yard. He took pleasure out of enjoying a sip of coffee before he responded.

"When you decided – for me – to do what you did, I was devastated. Remember when we were about to call it quits, and we started seeing Janet Andersen in counseling?"

He looked up to see if she was listening. She was still in her warrior pose, but the energy had drained away. She nodded slightly for him to go on.

"She said something that has stayed with me. Are you interested in hearing it, or do you want to keep defending your decision?"

Brian waited patiently for Christine to answer. Her eyes had a far off look as she desperately tried to remember what nugget of wisdom Janet had given to them that would have had this much of an impact. She ignored Brian's last statement and focused her memory on trying to identify what could have made such a difference to her husband.

She came up empty.

Brian saw the journey his wife had just taken down memory lane. Her face was transparent and fragile, as all of the emotions from those days swept over her again. He knew that she was still very much invested in her story that 'she did the right thing,' but his hope was that today's conversation may shake up that conviction.

Christine sighed in frustration, and wilted into her chair like a balloon that had just been popped, all of the air escaping slowly until there was nothing left. Her eyes closed as she fought to regain control of her emotions. When she finally looked back at Brian, all she noticed was the love and kindness in his eyes.

A fleeting thought crossed her mind – if he could find peace, why couldn't she?

Christine reached for her cup and held it nestled in both hands. After several moments, she asked, with slightly less sarcasm, "And what did the esteemed Janet Andersen tell you that you have thought about all of these years?"

Brian nodded at her attempt to listen. "She said that I shouldn't judge you for your decision." He paused as he remembered how long it took him to reach that point. "She also said to 'let God in' and I would find peace."

Christine sat up straight in her chair. "I don't remember her saying any of those things!"

Brian grinned playfully. "That's because you weren't there...I had several sessions with her on my own."

She didn't know whether to laugh or cry at this new information. She had no idea that Brian went to counseling by himself. A new thought occurred to her.

"When did you see her by yourself?"

"About a year ago."

The shock of that statement showed clearly on her face.

"But I thought she had given up being a marriage counselor when she became Principal of the High School."

Brian nodded. "She only spoke to me because of our past relationship. It was really as a friend, not as a counselor."

Christine was dumbfounded. She was living on the surface of life and had accepted that placidity in exchange for maintaining her "rightness" about the baby. Apparently, Brian had not accepted their life and was willing to take action to make changes.

That thought terrified her.

"Why now?"

"Because I was tired of just surviving. I don't feel that I am really living. I am ready to move forward and enjoy our life, but I couldn't do that as long as I was angry at you."

The shock waves seemed to keep coming at her. She felt unbalanced and suddenly, very much alone. Before she could stop herself, she cried, "But I think our life is great!"

Brian shook his head and said gently, "It is. But I want more. And I can't have a deeper relationship with you until we both get past this."

Christine sat still as a statue. When she finally spoke, it was with a dead voice.

"So you have 'gotten' past it and now you are waiting on me?"

"I wouldn't put it that cavalierly, but yes, I can say that I feel so much better."

The accusatory words flew out of her mouth. "Because you have forgiven me."

Brian's voice became very excited. "I had no idea what an impact it would have on me! When I invited God into the situation, it all became clear." He paused while he thought about his next words. "I finally came to grips with the fact that what you did was not really between you and me."

Frantic blue eyes flew to his calm brown ones. A gasp of air burst out of her mouth. She couldn't speak but waited for his next words, as if a death sentence was about to be pronounced.

"Your decision was between you...and God."

Christine flew out of her chair and stalked to the edge of the deck, back turned against the truth of her husband's words. Her arms crossed in front of her, trying desperately to hold onto the world as she knew it. Never in a million years did she dream that this conversation would force her to face the one person in the world she dreaded facing...herself.

It only took a millisecond for her defenses to spring back into place. She turned around and faced her husband, vibrating with pent-up energy.

"Keep your forgiveness to yourself, Brian. I am doing just fine without it."

With that pronouncement, she stalked off the deck and went back into the house. Brian sat on the deck for a little longer, then he quietly let himself out of the house. Christine heard him start his car and watch him back out of the driveway, not knowing where he was going.

What right did he have to tilt her world by his 'forgiveness'? Her defensiveness and anger had kept her going all of these years. How could he just change the rules and expect to follow obediently? That just wasn't fair...

Christine groaned and shifted in her bed as she tried to get comfortable. The scene that played out on the deck at the beginning of the summer kept haunting her, especially now that Brian had actually taken action and left. Was that what he was trying to tell her – that he could no longer stand living with her? Or was it something else?

It was as if they were playing tennis and he had just lobbed an easy ball to her. Now it was up to her to choose how to react. Should she smash it back, using her anger and bitterness as the fuel to protect herself? To react as she had always done – defensively, passionately rationalizing her actions.

Or was there another choice...a different way to react?

She felt anger boil up at Brian. How dare he change the rules of the game by forgiving her? Now that he had shifted his position on the baby, she had no one to defend her decision against. He had effectively pulled the rug created by her rationalizations out from under her and left her standing on naked ground.

Utterly alone.

With nothing more than her defenses and rationalizations to explain her behavior.

It was just like building a castle and holding it up for everyone to see, then discovering that it was really a castle made out of sand. A castle that was part of a beach that was shaped and formed by the ebb and flow of waves. A castle of no substance that dissolved when waves of forgiveness washed over it.

Her castle of beliefs had just crumbled.

Answers were as elusive as moon beams and just as slippery. Her life had fallen apart and she had no earthly clue how to put it back together. The music that had consoled her through these many years was still silent and left a vacant space in her mind. She tried humming the sad tune, but it fell flat and dead.

She sighed and again tried to get comfortable. Sleep would be a welcome escape from her thoughts and feelings. She was so tired of defending herself – first against Brian, now against Savanna.

Couldn't anyone see what her decision had cost her?

Christine finally got up out of bed and went to her bathroom. She kept a bottle of mild sleeping pills in her cabinet for emergencies. Well, this night surely qualified.

As she closed the mirrored door of the cabinet, she caught sight of herself in the reflection. Something made her pause and look more closely. As she stared at herself, one thought rose up in her mind.

One thought that had never appeared before. It was completely opposite her usual, habitual thought patterns about the baby and her role in that situation.

One thought made her pause and reconsider whether her present course was really what she wanted.

One thought that made the music stop.

She didn't realize it until just this moment. All through her tears, recriminations and self-pity, one thought clarified her current situation and put it all into perspective.

And terrified her at the same time.

Was being right about the baby worth losing her family?

10

To Love or to Fear; That is the Question

In life as in dance: Grace glides on blistered feet.
~ Alice Abrams

The rest of that week dragged by. Savanna still remained apart and alone from her other friends, but she found that she did not mind at all. Her mind was too preoccupied with everything that she had learned over the past week. Even the distance that Mia kept from her seemed trivial compared with her experiences in the forest, with Avery and then Ms. Andersen's complete acceptance of everything Savanna had shared with her.

Savanna felt like the script of her life had been altered dramatically, and she had to catch up and learn her new lines. It was unsettling and exhilarating, all at the same time. Everyone else was acting from the old script, but Savanna could no longer be that small.

Her life had shifted on its axis and she was still learning how to stay balanced.

She knew there was so much more to life than what appeared on the surface. The problem was learning how to integrate this new knowledge into her everyday routine. She had already experienced how quickly she could lose the connection with Love Divine when Mia had rejected her story. Savanna wanted to maintain her bubble of serenity, even in the face of someone else's anger, but she just did not know how to do it.

By the time Friday night rolled around, she was exhausted from trying to analyze everything that had happened to her. She had not sleep well and felt tired and cranky when she woke up the next morning. The only thought that cheered her was that it was Saturday and for once, she did not have that much homework.

After going to the bathroom and brushing her hair smooth again, she sat back down on her bed, looking out the window without seeing the gentle light filtering through the trees. Usually, Saturday mornings were spent eating cereal in front of the television, cartoons blaring loud enough to numb her mind. But this morning, she knew that would be a total waste of time.

She had to figure out what all of these experiences meant. How should she act at school? She couldn't try to explain her recent encounters with anyone else, especially after Mia's total and immediate rejection. She still was angry about her parent's separation, and especially about the fateful decision her mother had made so many years ago. What should she do about that? These questions plagued her constantly, until her head hurt and she groaned in frustration.

Savanna was about to give up and go downstairs when she saw her journal, lying on the bedside table, still open to the page where she had asked God a direct question. She suddenly remembered what had happened to her right after she asked if God was present.

"How can I be such an idiot?" she exclaimed as she grabbed her journal and pen, and sat down against her headboard. She took several minutes to breathe deeply and calm her mind. She was still unsure about this process, but realized that she did not have anything to lose and everything to gain. She carefully wrote down another direct question.

To God.

"Will you help me through this?"

The answer was immediate, swift and sure. She heard the same deep, low voice that she had heard earlier, except this time, it was as soft as the curtain that moved gently in the flow of air from the slightly cracked window.

"I am with you always, dear one."

The voice was like an embrace of pure love. Savanna dropped her pen and closed her eyes. She felt overwhelmed with all-consuming joy and knew that she had turned a corner in her spiritual life. And if what God had just told her was true...

In her mind, a great divide opened between her old life and the one that waited for her. It was a choice to play small, according to the world's rules and being miserable...or jumping over into a new realm of heart connectedness to God.

She jumped.

When Bandelier, the cat, landed lightly on her bed, Savanna looked at her in amazement. She had never really noticed the intricate pattern of color woven by various individual hairs. Bandelier's eyes were hazel and opaque, divided by the black vertical slit of her pupil. They gazed steadily at Savanna, intelligence and love shining brightly. Savanna sat mesmerized by the exquisite color she saw in the depths of her cat's eyes.

Who knew that beauty surrounded her all the time?

A gentle knock on the door disrupted her reverie.

"Savanna, it's time to get up," her mother said as she tentatively opened the door. Her head showed between the door and the frame, while her eyes searched Savanna's for a clue as to her daughter's mood.

Savanna looked at her mom. Really looked at her as a person with problems, struggles, uncertainties and doubts. She silently asked for guidance and support and instantly felt her anxiety lift. Although she was not sure how to handle her feelings about her mother, she knew that it was going to work out.

Ms. Andersen's voice replayed in her head. "Your parents can see a lot more of the screen than you can. It is not your place to judge them or their actions."

In the brief span of time that it took for these thoughts to flash across Savanna's mind, she made a decision. Savanna smiled at her mother and patted the bed, inviting her back into her life.

Christine's eyes swelled with unshed tears as she slowly crossed the room. Her weight on the edge of the mattress could never compare with the weight on her heart. Savanna saw the truth and gathered her mother into her arms. The reversal of roles was odd but authentic at the same time.

Christine was the first to pull away. "You don't hate me?" she asked tentatively.

Savanna shook her head. "I had a long talk with Ms. Andersen yesterday," she replied. "It really helped me see that I am not in a position to judge your actions."

Christine's look of shock quickly changed into relief. "What in the world did she tell you?"

Savanna shook her head. "It's a long story, but I love you and accept you, no matter what you did in the past."

"Savanna Hartt, what in the world has come over you?" cried her mother in astonishment.

Savanna just smiled and looked into her mother's eyes. She concentrated on sending waves of love to her mother, and she could actually glimpse the moment when her mother felt it.

Christine stood up quickly and broke the connection. She had to regain control over the situation and quickly reverted to her role as mother. As she turned to leave, she said, "Well, whatever you have been up to, it's time for breakfast. Please get dressed and come downstairs."

Savanna nodded to her mother's retreating back. Savanna smiled to herself, because she caught a glimpse of the fear in her mother's eyes. Savanna now knew exactly the course she would take with her mother. She would send waves of love to wash away the guilt and shame that had closed up her mother's heart for too long.

Perhaps, if Savanna was persistent and diligent enough, she could clear a space to help her mom heal and reunite their family.

That hopeful thought was enough motivation to propel Savanna out of bed, early on a Saturday morning. She took a moment to stretch and try to touch the ceiling. She winked at heaven and said "thank you" to God who had led her to this new understanding. Things were going to be O.K.

Unfortunately, Savanna did not count on adults who stubbornly held onto their stories, even when they no longer served them or anyone else.

As they sat down to eat breakfast, Savanna had a light bulb idea. "Mom," she said with excitement in her voice. "Why don't you come to the park with me today? We could ride our bikes and take a picnic lunch!"

Christine looked up from the newspaper she was reading and said, "I don't know if I have time. I have a million errands to run and..." She paused just long enough to look closely at her daughter. Savanna seemed too excited – like she wanted to show her something. Christine paused a moment, then said, "You know what? That sounds like a great idea!"

They cleaned up the kitchen and did some of the household chores that had piled up from the week. Christine hurried to the grocery store for more supplies and drinks. Their excitement grew stronger as they packed lunch and went out to the garage. Christine's bike was in a dark corner of the garage, but they hit a small snag when they noticed the front flat tire. "I guess I haven't ridden much lately," Christine said with chagrin. A quick pop of condensed air fixed the tire and they were off.

Brilliant morning sunlight reflected off the spokes of the wheels. Hair flew back in the breeze. Savanna and her mom rode side by side, and shared a look of utter joy at the experience of freedom.

"I forgot how fun this is!" cried Christine over the wind rushing past her.

Savanna just nodded and kept pumping her legs. They soon reached the park and Savanna led the way to her spot underneath the stately aspen grove, overlooking the placid pond.

Christine stopped short with disgust. "Why did you bring me here, young lady?" She demanded. "Are you trying to get me and your father back together again?"

The accusation hung heavy in the air. It did not disturb Savanna's peaceful attitude and soon the air was clear again. Savanna lay out the blanket on the soft ground and started setting out lunch.

"Why are you setting a place for three?" Christine's voice was getting higher and higher, as she suspected some trick was about to be played on her. She began looking around the park for signs of her husband, and a look of pure disappointment filled her eyes when he did not appear.

Savanna stopped fussing with the picnic and motioned for her mother to sit down. When Christine had settled, Savanna looked deeply in her mother's eyes again and waited for her mother to calm down. After several moments, Savanna nodded that it was time to begin.

She assumed the classic yoga position and closed her eyes, breathing deeply. In her mind, she began calling to Avery and Avatar. It was time for them to meet her mother.

Christine was shocked at the change in her daughter. She stared at her for a few moments, and was about to demand that Savanna stop this nonsense, when she saw a movement out of the corner of her eye.

Two figures appeared at the top of the hill, gliding toward them.

Christine looked from the two silhouettes back to her daughter, and understood intuitively that there was a connection. She watched her daughter closely, and saw only peace and joy written on her face. Christine decided to withhold judgment until she learned more about what was going on with Savanna and these two beings.

Just as Christine made that decision, Savanna stood up and raised her arms to heaven. "Mother," she began. "Meet Avery and Avatar!"

As soon as Christine turned around, Avery was standing about five feet away. Avatar barked at the mention of his name, and a long, graceful tail swung lightly in the breeze.

Christine jumped in surprise, and her mind went into shock. She looked back at the top of the hill, where she had first glimpsed them, then back to where they were standing under the old tree. It was not humanly possible to have covered that distance in the five seconds that had just passed.

Shock played with disbelief on Christine's face, until finally Avery smiled warmly in understanding and stood directly in front of Christine.

Avery smiled and bowed in respect. "I am a friend of your daughter's."

"Do you go to school with her?" Christine asked too harshly, her protective parenting instincts on full alert.

Avery gracefully sat down next to Savanna. The look they shared brimmed with love and they smiled at each other. Avery's adult hand found its way to Savanna's smaller, slender one. "You could say that," Avery answered.

Christine stood over the two and put her hands on her hips for emphasis. "Savanna, who is this person?" she said with as much disdain as she could muster.

Savanna was still smiling at Avery, a look of pure contentment on her face. "She is my friend," Savanna sighed dreamily. Savanna seemed lost in another time and there was no sign of her returning.

A look of alarm flashed over Christine's face. "Savanna Hartt, you stand up this instant!"

Savanna was shocked out of her reverie and looked at her mother in surprise. "What's the matter?" she cried, hurt and anger filtering through her voice and clouding the pure light that shone in her eyes.

Christine was in her full-battle-force Mother Protection Mode. She grabbed Savanna's hand and pulled her up. Avery closed her eyes at the disruption and said a silent prayer. Avatar growled a warning and jumped to his feet, ready to protect his master.

Savanna still did not understand what caused the disruption. One minute she was blissfully aware of her spirit connecting with the world, and especially Avery, then the next minute her mother was acting like a raving lunatic. Christine dragged her away from the tree and whipped her around to stare intently into Savanna's shocked eyes.

"Who is that person and how do you know her?" Christine demanded in a tone dripping with anger and acid.

Savanna could not bring herself to speak. She stared at her mother with a look that said, "You have just grown two heads," and she started to walk back toward Avery and her dog.

"Don't you walk away from me, young lady!" Christine was not going to accept defiance in this battle. She put all the authority she had into those eight words that drew a line in the sand.

Savanna paused for a tick of time, and then kept walking. She calmly sat down under the tree and smiled at Avery. Avery nodded at Savanna's mother, and said quietly to Savanna, "We should go. We will meet again soon." Avery stood up and she and her dog began to walk away. Only this time, they looked normal – just a young woman and her dog enjoying a nice walk on a Saturday morning - instead of floating above the ground as before.

Savanna could see the fear on her mother's face. Unfortunately, she underestimated the anger in her own heart. Anger trumped fear and a torrent of words spilled out of her mouth, madly out of control.

"How could you do that to me?" she cried. "Avery is my friend and you treated her like she was a piece of dirt!" Hurt and anger made Savanna's eyes hard as flint.

"I can't have you meeting strangers in the park!" Christine Hartt simply could not believe that her own daughter would be so careless. "What do you know about this woman?" she demanded, not a hint of flexibility in her voice.

Savanna was beside herself. "Who do you think has helped me through Dad leaving?" She cried as she grabbed her bike and jumped on. "You said you noticed a change in me – who do you think was responsible?"

Savanna did not wait for an answer. Instead, she pumped the pedals as fast as she could to get away from her mother. Christine stood next to the duck pond, her mouth slightly opened, staring at a daughter she no longer knew.

Silence descended on the area, while Christine pondered what to do. She couldn't return home right now – Savanna was too upset. Christine knew that she had over-reacted to Savanna's friend and she was already sorry for going ballistic. She was too quick to judge the situation and did not allow her daughter time to explain herself. A simple but profound mistake in Parenting 101. Christine sighed and decided to wait awhile before riding her bicycle home.

Christine realized that she had no place else to go at that moment in time. Her stomach grumbled a reminder, so she did the only sensible thing and sat down with the picnic blanket. She slowly ate bits and pieces from their lunch, tasting the bitterness of regret. If only she had not jumped so quickly to the wrong conclusion about Savanna's friend...If only she had held her tongue for a moment to study the situation...If only...

Christine sighed deeply and began to clear away the leftovers. As she reached for the empty soda bottle, she noticed a small piece of paper stuck to the side. She carefully peeled it off and slowly read the short heading and message.

Miracle Token – Universal Currency

You are holding a miracle of a moment in time. Use it wisely.

There was a photograph of a mosaic of blue, green and yellow tiles, which formed intertwined boxes. It instantly made Christine think of connections and relationships, but she was not sure why.

The paper seemed almost effervescent with energy. The simple declaration sent a jolt of energy through her body. Christine's mind stopped spinning for a moment and she felt lifted out of her body. It only took an instant of time, but it was enough for her to be frightened of a message that seemed so ordinary, yet had such an unusual impact on her.

Christine's mind tried to grasp what had just happened to her. Because there was no rational explanation, her mind dismissed the words as "crazy." But she could not stop herself from reading them again, wondering how they had affected her so quickly and on such a different level.

Simple instructions and website were written in the smallest font that was still legible.

Please add #MiracleToken to your Tweet to let me know you received this message. @MiracleIncome www.MiracleIncome.com

This was just too much! First Savanna's strange behavior, now a bizarre note that somehow found its way into her bag of groceries? Christine's frustrated sigh spoke volumes about the shape of her life in that moment. She had just reached her limit on the number of mysteries, unfathomable relationships and a failed marriage on top of it all.

The simple note was still in her hand. She was about to wad it up as if it were nothing, but something stopped her. Instead, she gently folded it and slipped into the pocket of her jeans. She would deal with it later, when she could go online and see if that website would explain the meaning of the note and how it got into her grocery bag.

The soft blanket, nestled in its bed of leaves, proved too strong a magnet for her. She lay down, settled herself and after several deep breathes, she let herself relax for the first time in years.

She began thinking back over the last week, wondering at the transformation of her daughter from an angry, rebellious teenager to a calm, self-assured young woman who was happy even when her family was falling apart.

What in the world could have caused such a dramatic transformation?

Christine's mind then drifted back to the scene at the kitchen table, when Brian quietly announced that he was moving out. Although her reaction was numbed shock, a small part of her had expected that to happen for years. She felt the same wash of anguish and frustration begin to engulf her, but just for a few moments, she decided not to go there.

Brian's decision to leave now made more sense. Her mind flew back to their talk on the deck at the beginning of summer, when he told her that he had "forgiven her." It seemed as if he had moved on, leaving her behind to stew in a mess of her own making.

The Judgment Voice that always showed up when she was at her lowest point emotionally began to tune up. She could not bear to listen to the same time-worn accusations, especially when the music was not there to console her. For the first time in years, she refused to listen.

And felt a small space open up inside of her.

Just for this moment, she wanted to enjoy the peacefulness of lying under the pines, listening to the wind and breathing the crisp, clear air.

Words from long ago popped into her head without warning or invitation.

"Your words are your wand, Chrissie," her mother reminded her, shaking her head. "Before you shoot off your mouth, just remember that your words have great power."

Chrissie, all of 16 years old and so sure of herself and her opinions that nothing could stop her, responded flippantly, "I don't believe in all that 'thought, word, deed' stuff! My dance teacher knows that I am the best student she has ever had. She should rot in hell for choosing Rebecca instead of me for the dance recital!"

It was the last comment, made in a similar tone and with identical intent that had prompted her mom to admonish her about the power of her words. Chrissie was so upset by her dance teacher's decision to choose her rival that she flagrantly dismissed her mother's sage advice.

"I don't care," Chrissie declared. "She's just an old wind bag anyway! She couldn't see real talent if it hit her on the nose!" With that, Chrissie left the room, but couldn't help adding under her breath, "I hope she gets hit by a car or something."

Hours later, Chrissie's mom knocked softly on the door to her room. "Honey, I need to talk to you," she called out. Chrissie was lying on her bed, talking on her phone (she had her own line) with another dancer who was also not chosen. They had been egging each other on, supporting each other and making mean comments about Rebecca and their dance teacher.

When Chrissie did not answer, her mother pushed open the door, a pained expression drawing her features together tightly. Chrissie was oblivious to her mother until she gently took the phone out of her hand and hung it up.

The reaction was immediate and swift. "MOTHER!" Hot, angry eyes flashed in a flushed face. "How could you do that? I was talking with Natalie and you just hung up on her!"

When Chrissie's mom did not react to her outburst, but instead sat down heavily on the bed, eyes downcast and shoulders slumped, it should have been a signal to Chrissie that something terrible had happened. But she missed the cues.

Chrissie continued her tirade until she finally ran out of breath. It was only then, in the silence that followed, that she stopped and looked at her mother. Really looked.

And knew something was wrong.

She sat down next to her mother and gently nudged her. Instead of nudging back, her mother took her hands into her larger ones, and turned slightly toward her daughter. Tears filled her eyes as she said the words that changed Chrissie's life forever.

"Your dance teacher was hit by a car this evening."

Chrissie looked at her in disbelief. Shock froze her features, but fear was sliding in to take its place. "Is she O.K.?" The question was whispered in the voice of a young child, ever hopeful that life would always have happy endings.

Her mom just shook her head, while liquid emotion streamed down her face, leaving a trail of sadness and pain.

"When?" was the only word she could choke out of her suddenly dry throat.

Her mother's look of compassion said volumes. They were both thinking the same thing, but neither one dared to say it. Chrissie knew the answer before she spoke, but something compelled her to ask anyway. "It was after I came up here, wasn't it?"

The knowledge of her responsibility weighed heavily on her for years. As time went by, she had almost convinced herself that her careless words were just a coincidence and not somehow connected to the fate of her dance teacher.

Almost.

Christine sighed heavily as the memories flooded back. She was so tired of feeling sad...so tired of feeling misunderstood and alone. And now, her hastily said words had hurt Savanna deeply. She hoped that the damage was not irreparable.

"No one understands me!" Anger mixed with deep sadness threatened to overwhelm her. "What can I do?" she moaned aloud. Somehow, inexplicably, her flippant words about her dance teacher and her actions to "protect" the baby seemed intertwined. Her mind desperately sought relief, but none was apparent. Her body was racked with guilt, tension and anger. And her spirit...her spirit was slowing slipping away.

Finally, she was spent, tired and defeated. She turned to the only other source of relief she could think of.

"I need help, God," Christine pleaded softly.

No answer came, at least not in the form that she expected. The wind seemed to pick up a little and one mountain jay stopped briefly to look down on her before continuing about his business. The world did not stop spinning just because she asked for help.

"So much for magical solutions," she thought ruefully. She knew that she still needed to give Savanna time to cool off before reasoning with her about meeting strangers in the park. The food she ate was making her sleepy, and she realized that she had nowhere else to go at that moment.

"Maybe I'll just close my eyes for a minute," she thought to herself as her body sank deeper and deeper into the blanket. The sounds of the wind in the trees and the ducks on the pond were a quiet symphony of relaxing melodies, all designed to lull her into a deep sleep. Her breathing and her heart rate slowed and she allowed herself to relax into another level of consciousness.

Suddenly, without warning, Christine found herself caught waist deep in a jello-like mass of goop. She tried to climb out of it, but her struggles only made her sink deeper into the sticky mess. She was beginning to panic when a hand appeared above her, stretched out and offering help. Christine grabbed the hand and used it to leverage her way out of the pool of slime.

"Thank you!" she gasped as she tried to get some of the sticky mess off her clothes.

Christine glanced up and stopped breathing. The most beautiful woman in the world stood in front of her! She was dressed in white, billowy clothes, her body was tall and slender and her eyes were hypnotizing. Christine could not pinpoint their color, but they were like magnets, pulling her into their mysterious depths.

Frantically, Christine looked quickly away and broke the connection. She managed to choke out the obvious question, "Who are you?"

The woman smiled and gestured away from the cesspool. "Shouldn't we go somewhere more comfortable?" she asked quietly.

Christine nodded and looked around her. Where was the duck pond? Where was her bicycle? Just as panic was about to overwhelm her mind, the woman spoke again, this time in a more demanding tone of voice.

"Christine Hartt, don't you think it is about time you gave up your story?"

Christine turned to look at the woman, astonishment written all over her face. Anger soon replaced it and she said in a scathing voice, "How dare you tell me what to do!"

The woman smiled knowingly and nodded. "Just as I thought," she murmured to herself as she sat down under a beautiful, stately oak tree.

One part of Christine's mind made a note about the oak tree. "I must be dreaming," she said to herself. "No oak tree would ever grow that tall in Colorado." Since she now knew that she was definitely dreaming, she decided to enjoy the experience.

"Who are you and how do you know my name?" she demanded a bit harshly.

The woman patted the ground beside her and said gently, "I will answer all of your questions, but you must first sit down so we may enjoy our visit."

Christine could feel her blood pressure rising at each word that flowed out of the woman's mouth. She felt threatened by this strange woman who seemed to know her so well. Her senses were on high alert, but she could not detect any physical threat. Instead, the invisible threat was a direct assault to her emotions.

Not knowing what else to do, Christine flopped down on the ground, a heavy sigh escaping her lips.

"Not as graceful as when you were a dancer, are you?" The woman did not make this statement with any judgment or rancor; instead, it was said with calm observation of one who has seen better and was simply commenting on the difference.

"How did you know I used to be a dancer?" Christine was feeling more and more like she had jumped down the rabbit hole after Alice. She quickly looked around to see if a Cheshire cat was watching her every move.

The woman laughed delightedly. The sound was like a musically toned wind chime and the melodious notes seemed to rain down on them.

"Oh, Chrissie, you do have the best sense of humor!"

Christine's eyes grew wide in surprise and her mouth fell open. After several heartbeats, she looked closer at this woman who seemed to know so much.

"The only way you could know that nickname was if you grew up with me," she said in a whisper.

The woman threw back her head and laughed so loudly that several crows who were sitting above them flew off the branches in surprise, cawing their annoyance. Her laughter spread throughout the park, and it was several minutes before she managed to regain control of herself.

Christine did not look amused. Instead, her irritation grew exponentially, as each moment that passed was encased in laughter. The woman sensed that she was about to lose the attention of her student, so she calmed instantly and smiled at Christine.

"You were saying?" she prompted Christine gently.

Christine was about to jump up when a hand stayed her movement. As she looked down at the hand resting on her arm, Christine realized that the woman had just saved her from certain death in the slime pool. She closed her eyes and took several deep breaths, feeling her irritation give way to calm. The hand stayed on her forearm until Christine was relaxed and in control. Then it retreated quietly back to its owner.

"I can see that I will have to ask you direct questions and not get upset at the answers," Christine said with conviction. "So here goes – what did you mean about it being time for me to give up my story?"

The woman nodded in approval. "Good! We are going to skip past all the boring, 'Who are you and how do you know my name' and get to the good stuff." She paused to make sure her student was listening and said, "Would you agree that you have a story that you have kept alive all of these years?"

A look of shock filtered over Christine's face and then realization dawned. She looked away in shame so this lovely woman would not see her pain. The futile movement provided an affirmative answer to a question that Christine had never bothered to ask herself.

After a few moments, Christine gathered herself and turned back to the woman. She nodded and smiled slightly and gestured for the woman to continue.

"Good!" cried the woman, a bright smile lighting up her face with a glow of light. She turned so that she faced Christine squarely, and asked gently, "Is your story true?"

Christine felt anger rise up and it fueled her reaction. "What do you mean, is it true? Of course it's true!" she cried, her voice tinged with anger and frustration.

The woman shook her head and then gently asked, "Are the thought and judgments you created around the events true?"

"You mean I created my own story?" Christine asked incredulously.

"Of course! That is the way it works. You live through circumstances or events and then create a story around them to reflect back to you how you interpreted those events." She paused to see if Christine was following her explanation. "Then you create an additional layer of thoughts that rationalize the events, and together, these become your story. Your story becomes your filter through which you interpret future events. But the starting place for all of this was your experience of the original event, which is neutral."

Silence hung in the air as Christine tried to assimilate these new concepts. The woman waited patiently for more questions, which did not take long.

"How can an event be neutral when it affects each person who experiences it?"

The woman smiled knowingly and answered, "Think of it like a small pebble falling into a still, calm pool of water. The consequence of the pebble hitting the surface will always be to disturb the water's surface and cause ripples to spread out from the center. The rock fell and the water was momentarily disturbed." She paused for effect. "Was that a good thing or a bad thing? Or was it just an event with nothing attached to it until someone observed it and said it was good or bad?"

Christine's mind flashed back to her philosophy class in college. Her professor asked a similar question, but it had to do with the famous inquiry, "If a tree fell in the woods and no one was there to hear it, did it make a sound?"

Christine pulled her knees into a hug and started rocking like a child. The physical movement seemed to calm her mind as she considered what the woman had just said. Her mind drifted back over all of the words, accusations and pain caused by her original decision to "protect" her baby. She seemed to watch the replay from a distance, as if she were at a play, sitting in the audience while the actors carried out their roles on stage.

After several minutes, Christine stopped abruptly and asked, "I can see that I interpreted the events differently than my husband, and how my version drove us apart." She paused and then added vehemently, "But my story is exactly what happened!"

Laughter sprang from the woman's throat in waves of love. "Oh Chrissie, you are so stubborn!" Her slender hand reached out, palm open in invitation. The silent acceptance was more than Christine could handle. And the woman was laughing at her again!

Christine would have jumped up right then in her usual fit of anger, but something about this woman was familiar. Too familiar. She studied the face turned towards her, and actually saw a tiny image of herself reflected in those calm and loving eyes!

Just as a strange thought was starting to form in her awareness, the woman held out her other hand in a gesture of friendship. Christine forgot about the strange sense of connection she felt with this person, and smiled slightly. She felt a little off balance but decided that it could not hurt to take the woman's hand.

She was completely unprepared for what happened next.

The second that her fingers touched the woman's long, slender hands, a shot of energy burst up Christine's arms, across her chest and into her heart. She gasped and leaned back against the sturdy strength of the oak tree, breathing hard and desperately trying to calm the mad racing of her heart. Christine jerked her hands away from the fire of the physical contact and they flew to her heart in the universal gesture of protection.

The woman watched Christine's distress calmly, with a detached attitude. She waited for her student to begin breathing normally and then asked her question again, "Are you sure that your story is true?"

The blast of energy actually blew away Christine's usual defenses. Her mind - usually so filled with judgmental thoughts and beliefs - was quiet, stripped momentarily of its power. She thought for a moment and let her answer spring from her heart. "My story is true for me," she said, amazed at herself for taking one step away from defending her version of the events surrounding the baby.

"Exactly!" cried the lady, joyfully clapping her hands in delight at the insight of her student.

Christine looked at her in surprise. "Are you saying that my story isn't the truth?"

"Remember what I just said? All events are just that – an event in time and space. They are neither good or bad, right or wrong, commendable or despicable. It's your interpretation of the event that makes it true for you."

A puzzled look came over Christine's face. "But if I believe that it's true, doesn't that make it true?"

Laughter rang out again. "That is the beautiful paradox of life! You get to decide what is true for you."

Christine could not wrap her mind around what the woman was saying. Her thoughts were still quiet and the critical voice that usually dissected her words and actions was strangely mute. She felt something begin to rise in her that she had not felt in a long time. At first, she did not know what to call it but she enjoyed the strange feeling as she puzzled over the woman's words.

"Then what is the point of it all if I get to choose what something means to me?" The question spilled almost involuntarily from her lips, as she wrestled with the new concepts.

The woman smiled gently and said, "That is why you are here, at this time and in this place. To decide what it all means to you. You choose your reaction to everything that happens to you. It is your choice and your responsibility for the consequences." She paused thoughtfully and added, "Remember, if you don't like something, you can change your perception of it."

"I have been miserable and so unhappy about what I did," Christine admitted. "But what else could I have done?" Christine's entire being filled with anguish, guilt and despair, and she felt like she was standing on the edge of a cliff, about to let go and fall into the bottomless depths of nothingness.

The woman nodded and looked deep into Christine's troubled gaze. Christine felt as if she was looking into the mirror at herself. In a flash of insight, she instantly saw all the pain, anguish and separation that her story had caused those around her. Her deep seated guilt over her decision to end her pregnancy had spilled over and deeply affected those she loved the most. Bottomless shame and regret threatened to overwhelm her, but she suddenly remembered the wise words this mysterious woman had just spoken.

"Events happen, you interpret them and then you judge them. That becomes your story."

Christine felt removed from what she observed about her past. Having caught a glimpse of the tsunami of pain caused by her decision to not become the mother of a severely disabled child, the impact was plain to see. The question now was whether Christine would accept responsibility for her decision, forgive herself and grow from it, or would she continue to be caught in the vortex of guilt and frustration?

She recalled the searing thought that had flashed across her mind last night, as she was staring at herself in the mirror.

Was being right about the baby worth losing her family?

This was a defining moment. A crossroad that presented two paths. And it was totally her decision which one to take.

She could continue with her story and lose everyone she loved, or she could accept it as part of her own journey and start a new chapter of her life.

She chose life.

Christine closed her eyes and prayed. Without pretense, without manipulation. Just a simple prayer to God for his love, forgiveness and guidance. She released her tight hold on her story and let it go. In her mind, it became almost smoke-like, wispy tendrils flowing up and out of her mind.

To God.

Deep, heart-sore sobs racked her body as the floodgates opened. All of the pain, anguish, hurt and anger over her decision to not have the baby flooded her body. The mere act of not resisting the powerful emotions allowed them to flow through and out of her system.

After the storm of emotions had passed and she began to regain some control, Christine realized that she no longer felt suffocated and encased in her own bubble of misery. The cleansing process took Christine to a new space of compassion – for herself and for those caught up in her story. She recognized how fiercely she had defended her version of the events, and how that drove a steel wedge between herself and Brian. Relief flowed through her as she accepted the consequences of her actions.

"I am going to be O.K.," she thought to herself in amazement.

When she felt calm enough to return to the present moment, she realized that the woman was still sitting beside her. Christine felt immediate embarrassment over losing control in front of a total stranger. "Sorry about that," was all she could mumble.

The woman smiled gently and nodded. The next words out of her mouth rocked Christine's world, which was already teetering unbalanced. Her usually predictable orbit was completely skewed, and she felt disoriented and off kilter.

"Why did you really end your pregnancy, Christine?"

The birds seemed to pause, waiting for her answer. The wind no longer rustled the trees and the earth held its breath.

Why did she take such a solitary, finite course - one that could only end poorly for all concerned? She let the question settle on her, and because her mind was finally still, she waited patiently for the answer to burble up from her subconscious. It took several minutes, but when the answer came, she was completely seared through with the truth.

"I didn't want to be a mother to a child with such severe disabilities."

The statement hung in the air, shimmering with the clarity of truth. Tears flowed again, unnoticed by either woman, as Christine continued in a soft whisper. "I just wanted to be free from the nightmare," she finished lamely, shame written all over her face.

The woman nodded in acceptance. Then she asked softly, knowing that for Christine to finally heal and grow from her decision, she had to answer one final question.

"Did you act out of love...or fear?"

The question hung in the air, suspended in a moment of defining purpose. Would Christine have the courage to take the final step toward healing, or would she stay small and drive away everyone she loved? She faced another crossroads decision – would she continue to deny her spiritual self or would she accept the actions and consequences that resulted from decisions made by her ego-driven self?

Christine had come this far and was not about to give up now, even though this was the hardest question that she had ever faced. Asking whether she acted out of love or fear brought everything into sharp focus. Christine shook her head as she realized that she did not have a clue what she was doing when she made the decision to see the alternative doctor. Her total lack of self-awareness about such a life-altering decision was amazing.

She thought back to that time when her world was turned upside down. She and Brian were so happy about the pregnancy and had made all kinds of plans for their new family. When the doctor told them about their baby's severe disabilities, Christine simply shut down. Mentally, physically and emotionally. She could not fathom why they were going through such a horrific experience and she decided to do whatever it took to remedy the situation.

Even if it meant killing their child.

Without telling Brian.

Had she acted out of love, just as she tried to convince everyone and herself that she made the right decision? Or did she allow fear to dominate her thoughts and actions, never considering the permanent consequences?

"You know the answer to that question," Christine said, stalling for time.

"You're right, I do. The real question is whether you know." The words were spoken in a tone that brooked no doubt of their veracity.

Pain painted its harsh brush over Christine's fine features. She closed her eyes and clenched her hands in frustration. Was her motivation really not from love, as she had tried to convince everyone, or more from fear? Her heart knew the answer before her mind did.

"Fear," she whispered to herself, closing her eyes while she felt like sinking into the earth and never being alive again. Guilt threatened to overwhelm her, but suddenly she felt lifted up from her anguish, free of sadness and pain. Her eyes flew open in surprise and she looked at the woman, who was now kneeling over her, her hands hovering just over Christine's head.

"What did you just do to me?" Christine asked incredulously.

Deep concern mixed with amusement played out in the woman's eyes. She sighed and said, "Good. For a moment I thought I had lost you." She waited for Christine to say something more, and then asked softly, "How do you feel?"

Christine considered her internal state of affairs and then said with a laugh, "Better than I have felt in years!" She reassessed herself for any remaining emotional debris, and discovered to her delight that she felt lighter and freer.

"You are a magician!" she cried with happy abandon.

The woman shook her head and sighed. "I would have come to you sooner, but you had to ask for me." She looked deep into Christine's eyes and asked, "Do you believe your story now?"

Surprise flashed across Christine's face. "No!" she declared happily. She paused and took an internal inventory of her thoughts, emotions and beliefs about the baby. After several heartbeats, Christine gasped when she realized the truth. "I don't have that story anymore!" she declared to herself and to the world. Joy and gratitude filled all the places in her heart that were isolated and barren moments before. The transformation was instantaneous.

Suddenly, Christine jumped up gracefully and pulled the woman up too. Then she grabbed the woman's hands and began to dance a happy jig around the trunk of the oak tree. The women laughed and danced to a timeless melody.

Finally, the joyful energy that fueled Christine's happiness ran out. Heavy breathing and damp foreheads were the tangible results of their dancing. They sat down again and smiled at each other.

"Now will you tell me who you are?" Christine asked with a twinkle in her eye.

The woman laughed to the sky. "Christine Hartt, you mean after having gone through the most amazing experience of your life, you still have not figured out who I am?"

Christine shook her head slowly, closely studying her new friend. A shimmering thought formed in her mind, but she dismissed it immediately. As she continued to study this woman, the disturbing thought would not leave. Finally, Christine decided to throw it out there and see what happened.

"Are you my spiritual self?" she asked tentatively.

The woman clapped her hands once, gave a subtle wink of acknowledgement and disappeared in a flash of brilliant light.

The world seemed to tilt on its axis. Christine opened her eyes and looked in confusion at the duck pond, the remnants of her lunch scattered around her. She still lay on the picnic blanket under the pine trees, but she felt light-headed, almost as if she had traveled a long way and had just returned. When she took a quick inventory of her emotions, she discovered to her delight that the heavy mantle of guilt and sorrow no longer threatened to suffocate her. What in the world happened to her?

Christine felt too disorientated to stand, but managed to pull herself up into a sitting position. Just as wisps of her dream started coming back to her, Christine heard a familiar voice.

"Mother, are you alright?" Savanna asked in concern.

Christine turned towards her daughter and smiled as warmly and lovingly as she could. "Oh honey, I am so sorry for hurting you in front of your friend!" She opened her arms and held Savanna close and they both cried.

"I don't know how many more tears I can cry," Christine finally said. Savanna pulled away from her with a questioning look, but Christine held up her hand and said quietly, "Let's go home and I will tell you what happened."

She paused as more memories started to come back to her. She shook her head and smiled reassuringly at her daughter. "Everything is going to be O.K.," she said, more to herself than to Savanna. "I am going to be O.K.," she added in her mind, wonder and hope bursting forth from her long frozen heart.

They packed up the rest of the lunch and slowly pedaled home, silently rolling toward a new life.

11

Can You Change in an Instant?

There are short-cuts to happiness, and dancing is one of them. ~Vicki Baum

After they reached the house, Savanna waited patiently for her mother to explain what happened in the park. Subtle changes were apparent, but Savanna could only guess at her mother's different energetic presence.

Christine led her daughter into the den and they both sat down, facing each other on the sofa. Christine took the slender fingers of her daughter's hand and held it gently between her two larger ones, sandwiching it with love. Savanna smiled at the image with understanding and looked into her mother's eyes, which glowed with a new light.

"I'm sure you are wondering what happened to me in the park after you left." Christine looked away, embarrassed at her rude behavior towards her daughter.

Savanna nodded and stayed quiet, intuitively recognizing that her mother had experienced a seismic shift in her perspective. While they sat and listened to the peaceful house, a thought crossed Savanna's mind that she could not keep to herself.

"Did Avery and Avatar come back and talk to you?" she asked hopefully.

The question seemed to jar Christine back to the present. "No, that's not what happened," she said a bit impatiently.

Savanna shrugged her slender shoulders and asked, "Then what did happen?"

Christine shook her head and sighed heavily. "I am really not sure how to describe this, so I guess I will just tell you as best as I can and hope you believe me." She glanced at her daughter to see what her reaction would be to that last statement.

Savanna burst out laughing, then covered her mouth when she realized that she might have hurt her mother's feelings. She put her other hand on top of the rest and squeezed as hard as she could. "I wasn't laughing at you," Savanna cried. "If you knew everything that has happened to me this week, you would have a hard time believing it too!"

The shocked look on Christine's face was quickly replaced by understanding. She took a moment to think back on all the events that had happened in Savanna's life in the last seven days. Her father left them, trouble at school, caught cheating on a test, suspended for two days...

"Oh honey," Christine said with concern. "I was so focused on myself that I have not thought about what you have been going through." Tears formed in Christine's blue eyes as guilt flooding her being.

Savanna shook her mother's arm fiercely. "No, don't choose that!" Savanna's pleading, desperate begging making her voice rise in pitch.

Christine heard the anxiety in her daughter's voice and managed to sputter, "But I am your mother! I am supposed to think about you before myself." Fresh sobs racked her body as she acknowledged another failure in her life.

Savanna immediately took control of the situation and said in as commanding a voice as she could, "You don't have to choose to feel guilty. Choose differently!"

Christine's downward slide on the guilt train abruptly halted. Her eyes flew up to her daughter's, and the intensity in them was enough to shock Christine back into awareness.

She took a deep, cleansing breath and said quietly, "You're right."

The bird clock in the kitchen ticked steadily for several minutes, until it hit 1:00 p.m. A cardinal's birdsong filled the house as mother and daughter smiled at each other.

Christine smiled and asked gently, "Do I get a second chance?"

Savanna nodded and squeezed her mother's hand in support. No words were necessary and the love that passed between them was a palpable energy that filled the room.

Christine started again. "After you left, I knew I had made a terrible mistake. You found someone else to help you through this time." Christine paused then continued in a softer voice, "I guess it hurt because it wasn't me." Christine chanced a glance at Savanna to gauge her reaction. Savanna nodded in understanding and smiled her encouragement to her mother to continue.

"I could not come home right then since you needed time to cool down. So I decided to take advantage of the lovely day and take a nap under the aspens."

Christine allowed herself to be pulled back into the events that happened earlier that day, and she sat quietly, a soft smile on her face. After several moments, Savanna prompted her to finish the story.

"I had a dream," Christine finally continued. "And I met..." She stopped as she felt the first lick of anxiety. She risked another look at Savanna, but instead of seeing disbelief, Savanna small face reflected only peace and understanding.

Christine paused while she gathered herself. She finally whispered, "I think I met my spiritual self."

Savanna clapped her hands together in joy. "How wonderful!" she cried.

Christine's jaw fell opened, as she stared in astonishment at her daughter. "I thought you would laugh at me," she said.

Savanna shook her head and said ruefully, "I would have before last week, but since Dad left, I have had some amazing experiences."

Now everything made sense. Savanna's new found calmness, her solid sense of self in the midst of their family crisis. Christine understood on an intuitive level that Savanna must have had her own encounter with her spiritual self. Whatever all of this meant, Christine was grateful to God for reaching out to them when they needed to know he was there.

Christine looked at her daughter more closely, and saw the same love reflected in her eyes that she had seen in her dream. In a flash of insight, she knew that the thread connecting both was... love. A sense of peace settled on her, providing strength to continue with their conversation.

"Did you have to answer the question about love or fear?" she asked hesitantly.

Savanna's smile lit up the room. "No, I never got to that question," she explained. "I started out asking 'why' questions and I discovered that those always lead to a dead end."

Christine smiled in recognition of the futility of 'why' questions. She closed her eyes as she remembered asking that very question of God during the time immediately before the abortion. It was because she never received any answers that she took the next step. A searing new thought struck her.

"You mean if I had stopped asking 'why' and started asking different questions, I might have seen the entire situation differently?" Christine stunned look spoke volumes. It was patently obvious that she had never considered that there may have been another reason for the baby's deformities.

Never, in a million years, had it occurred to her.

Savanna felt instant judgment rising in her, but took a deep breath and moved passed it. She considered her mother's anguished plea and asked for guidance to say the words that would lead to healing and acceptance.

"I still don't have it all figured out," Savanna said slowly. "But as soon as I stopped asking God why this was happening to me, and I asked for help instead, I was able to finally listen for the answer."

Christine thought about the wisdom of her daughter's words. She could now see how she became locked in a world that seemed like a dead end, except for a final, life-ending decision that appeared to be the only solution. At the time, she never considered that she might have misinterpreted the events that created the need for her decision. Instead, she had tried to solve it herself, shutting out both Brian and God.

In that order.

Fresh waves of sorrow racked her body as she finally released all of the pent up emotional debris from so long ago. Savanna sat quietly, her arms around her mother, as the liquid pain flowed freely.

Finally, the storm was over.

Savanna stood up and went to the kitchen for Kleenex. Christine gratefully accepted the tissues and started cleaning up the damage caused by her emotional tsunami. She smiled up at her daughter, and said softly, "Thank you."

Savanna smiled and helped her mother stand up. Christine was slightly unsteady on her feet, and they both agreed that she needed to lie down for a few minutes. As Christine passed through the kitchen, she paused to throw out the used tissues from her pockets. She was about to toss them in the trash when she felt the sharper edge of paper inside the soft folds.

"I almost forgot about this," Christine muttered softly, reading the note again.

Savanna's puzzled look prompted Christine to hand her the note. Savanna felt the slight jolt of energy as soon as the paper touched her skin, and her focus was intent as she slowly opened the small piece of paper.

You are holding a miracle of a moment in time. Use it wisely.

Savanna glanced up at her mother for an explanation, but all Christine could do was shrug her shoulders. "I don't know what it means," she said softly.

Savanna continued to study the words, thinking back over everything that had happened in the last week. "How did you get this?" she asked her mother gently.

Christine smiled ruefully and said, "After you left the park, I finished our lunch. While I was packing up, I found this note inside the grocery bag."

Savanna looked down at the note, which seemed to glow slightly. She shook her head and asked softly, "Do you think it was meant for you?"

Her mother nodded silently. She had no rational explanation and her logical mind shut down at the myriad of possibilities of how that type of note had found its way into *her* grocery bag, on the exact day when she would be open and receptive to its message.

Savanna could see that her mother was about at the end of her physical resources. She suggested that they continue upstairs so Christine could lie down. As they walked up the staircase, an inspired thought caused Savanna to ask, "Do you mind if I keep the note to show to Avery?"

Christine almost slipped back into "protective mother mode," but caught herself just in time. She smiled at her own defensive reaction and said, "Of course." She paused on the step as another thought occurred to her. She turned around to her daughter and admonished, "But you have to promise to tell me exactly what Avery says about it!"

Savanna's grin was all the acknowledgment she needed. She tucked the note into her pocket and they continued up the stairs to the master bedroom. Savanna took off her mother's shoes and pulled down the shades to block the bright sun. She leaned over and gently kissed her mother on the forehead and left on soft feet, gently closing the door.

As Savanna slowly went back downstairs to eat some lunch, she heard the quick chirp of the house alarm from a door that had opened. Her first thought was, "Good. Dad's home," but then she remembered that this was no longer his home. Sadness instantly threatened to overwhelm her, but she was more proficient at recognizing the trigger and knew what was coming. Savanna took a deep breath to center herself and said to herself, "I am a beloved child of God." The thought instantly cheered her and she continued down the stairs to see who had come into the house.

As she turned the corner to go into the kitchen, she almost ran into her dad. They both stopped at the last second to avoid a collision and laughed. Savanna smiled warmly and reached up her arms for a hug, just as she used to do when she was six and her father was the hero in her world. Brian did not hesitate and scooped her up, squeezing her tightly.

"What are you doing here today?" Savanna asked as he let her down to the floor.

"I left several messages for you and your mother to ask if I could come over and get some things," he responded, exasperation lightly coloring his words. The mere fact that he had to ask permission to enter his own home had still not completely resolved itself in his mind. He added as an afterthought, "When I didn't hear back from either of you, I decided to come over and make sure that you guys are O.K."

Savanna nodded and gently pulled her dad into the kitchen. She motioned for him to sit at the counter while she started making sandwiches. Brian obeyed without asking questions, more from curiosity than from obedience. He noticed subtle changes in Savanna and he wanted to discover what was going on in her head. If she was going to feed him at the same time, so much the better.

He watched her silently as she created two turkey and Swiss sandwiches and arranged dark red grapes and strawberries on the side. She was totally focused on her task, but a happy energy flowed from her. Finally, when she set the food down in front of him and sat down next to him at the counter, he couldn't wait another minute to find out what was going on.

"How come you guys didn't answer my call or my text messages?"

Savanna said a silent prayer over the food, and then took a huge bite out of her sandwich. She grabbed a napkin to cover her mouth, from which bread and mayonnaise threatened to spill. She kept chewing to get through the mass of food and held up her index finger in the universal gesture of "wait just a minute." Finally, after a huge drink of water, she was able to answer.

"Sorry about that," she said with an apologetic grin. "I was starving and had to take a bite!"

Brian nodded in understanding and started to eat his own sandwich. His soft brown eyes looked with love on his only child, as he waited patiently to hear her explanation.

Savanna bit into a juicy grape and said, "We rode to the park on our bikes." She wiped grape juice of her chin and continued. "Mom and I had a fight and I came back home. She stayed in the park and fell asleep. I went back to check on her and we just got home." Savanna stopped to enjoy a strawberry. "She is upstairs taking a nap."

"Is she O.K.?" Brian's face creased in concern, but then he remembered he was not supposed to be involved anymore. He couldn't help himself as he added, "Your mother never likes to take naps. I am the one who is the 'Napster,' not your mother!"

Savanna raised her eyebrows at her father's strident tone. "Dad, it's not an emergency. Something happened to her in the park and she is trying to figure it out, that's all." Savanna fully expected her explanation to calm down her father, but instead, it had the opposite effect.

He blew up.

"What are you hiding from me, young lady?" he said in his sternest, "father" voice. He jumped off the stool and began to rush upstairs. He completely forgot to be disengaged and uninvolved. All of his protective instincts were on full alert and they centered on his wife. "If your mother is in trouble, I want to know about it," he said over his shoulder as he passed through to the hall.

Savanna started to get up and try and stop him, but she was too late. She heard his heavy footsteps on the stairs and the door to her parents' bedroom open. Savanna knew that her parents had a lot of things to work out, and she decided that she had done her part. She took her plate of food and glass of water, and went outside to sit on the patio chairs to enjoy her lunch in peace and quiet.

Upstairs, as Brian burst into their bedroom he noticed the darkness of the space. He took a moment to assess the situation and discovered that instead of sensing depression and sadness, he felt calm and peaceful. His observation was confirmed by the look on Christine's face as she slept.

She was actually smiling in her dream!

It had been many years since he had seen her look that way. Actually, now that he thought about it, it must have been before the baby...

His train of thought stopped abruptly as he considered the possibilities. A sprig of hope flowered in his chest at the thought that she might have forgiven herself for her past actions. He was lonely at the apartment and really wanted to return home to his family, but he could no longer act as the neutral buffer to Christine's emotional baggage.

When he finally made the decision to leave his family, he vowed to himself to not come back until she took responsibility for what happened. Forgiveness had done so much for him, that he wanted the same thing for his wife, so she could finally heal. Living at half speed was no longer acceptable to him, and he knew that the only way to move forward was to move through the pain. He had given up any hope that Christine would also learn that lesson.

Until this moment.

What in the world could have happened to Christine in the park to make her actually take a nap in the middle of the afternoon? It was unheard of for her to stop and rest. Brian always took at least one nap a day on the weekends, and Christine and Savanna always called him "The Napster." Affectionately, of course.

Brian was still unsure what had happened, but decided to wait until she woke up. He lowered himself in the reading chair by the window and leaned his head back on the cushion. "Maybe I will take a little nap too," he thought to himself as he drifted off to sleep.

Sometime later, his snoring woke him up. Brian sat up slowly in the chair, unsure of where he was or why he had decided to take a nap in the chair instead of his own bed. It was still almost pitch black and he had trouble making out any shapes or colors. He was just going through an internal body scan to determine what parts were going to be sore, when Christine opened the door and came out of the bathroom.

The light from the bathroom spilled out into the room, touching his shoes. Brian looked up at his wife, whose eyes were wide in shock at finding him in the bedroom. He waited so she could catch her breath, and then asked gently, "How are you, honey?"

Christine's hand touched the towel wrapped around her head, as if she thought he shouldn't see her like this. She was dressed in casual clothes – comfortable jeans, cotton fleece sweatshirt. No makeup and no fuss, just the way she loved to be on the weekends.

After her dream in the park and her conversation with Savanna, Christine still felt as if she had accidentally fallen down the rabbit hole. Her world was different – almost as if it was fresh and new. It was as if she was an alien from a strange planet who never learned the rules of this new game. In the newness lay her joy and happiness, but she could not yet bring herself to trust it. Not yet.

She sat down rather heavily in the other chair and sighed deeply.

"That is just the question I have been asking myself, ever since we got back from the park," she responded, more to herself than to him.

Brian waited and watched. He was still unsure about his wife, but she did seem much different from the frustrated, angry woman he had left last week. This person sitting in front of him reminded him of the Christine he fell in love with so many years ago at college. Her face was scrubbed clean, her blue eyes were clear and bright and she no longer had the mantle of depression that had become second nature to her.

Brian decided to play it light. "Who *are* you and what have you done with my wife?" he asked in a teasing tone.

Christine reacted to the words if not the message behind them. "I AM your greatest good – I AM your wife," she said in a deep falsetto voice, quoting from one of their favorite movies, "The Incredibles."

The playful exchange reminded Christine that she truly missed Brian and his presence in her life. Without thinking, she smiled at him and opened her hands in invitation.

Seconds passed while Brian stared down at her long, slender fingers. His mind could not grasp the new Christine, but his heart leapt in his chest at this unexpected turn of events. He gathered both of her hands in his larger ones and brought them up to his lips, where he kissed them tenderly.

The unexpected physical action was too much, too fast, too soon. "Stop it, Brian!" she cried as she jerked her hands away.

Fear entered her eyes as she remembered that he had forgiven her. Even after what she did, he forgave her. She didn't deserve such grace...she was too selfish and...

She slid down the crevasse of self-hatred and loathing without a whimper. The mask of indifference fell into place, hiding a seething caldron of pure shame, deep disgust and bitter anger. Brian reeled back from the transformation and looked at her in surprise.

"I thought you had finally moved on," he said tightly, clenching his fist in frustration. "But I can see that you are still stuck in your misery." He stood up and turned to go. "Let me know when you have it all figured out." He did not wait for an answer, but left quickly. The temptation to slam the door to emphasize his point was too much – it felt good to release a bit of his anger.

The door slamming against its jamb was a wake-up call. Christine froze in horror until that noise cut through her defenses and she remembered what happened to her in the park. She jumped up from the chair and rushed after him downstairs, the towel slipping from her head unnoticed. Just as she reached the front door and opened it, his car pulled away from the curb, tires spinning just a little on the concrete. Her shoulders slumped in defeat and she turned to go back inside, when Savanna blocked her way.

"What happened?" Savanna asked in concern.

Christine shook head and slowly walked back inside. She felt mechanical and wooden, as if all the joy and love she had just rediscovered was an illusion that was easily blown away. Her depression settled on her again, and her world turned grey.

Would she ever be free of this nightmare?

12

Eyes Wide Open for the First Time

Dance is the hidden language of the soul. ~ Martha Graham

Christine slowly headed for the kitchen and began to make tea, her movements automatic and habitual. Savanna waited for a signal that her mother wanted to talk, and when two cups were placed on the counter, she smiled to herself. She sent waves of love to both of her parents and hummed softly as she carried both cups outside to the deck.

Two lounge chairs waited in silent sentry to the beautiful view of the backyard. The tall pine trees lined the edge, the tops dancing in the wind high above the ground. The white slender trunks of aspens added a bright contrast to the darker pines. The aspen leaves no longer shimmered in the sunlight, but instead lay on the ground, covering the open area that had already turned brown, ready for winter. The usually vibrant flower beds and pots were banked and silent, waiting for their first blanket of snow.

Christine sighed as she gazed over the backyard. "When did the aspens change and why did I miss it?" she wondered to herself. She felt like she had been asleep for a very long time, and just now, she had woken up to see an unfamiliar world.

After they were seated and her mother sipped from the hot liquid, Savanna spoke.

"He was concerned about you – he thought something bad happened to you in the park," she explained gently. Savanna could guess what happened upstairs, but she wanted her mother to recognize what happened when she chose fear instead of love.

"I know," Christine said softly. "I woke up feeling wonderful and went to take a shower. He was sleeping in the chair and I didn't realize it until I came out of the bathroom." She added lamely, "He startled me."

Savanna nodded in sympathy and took a sip of her tea. She knew how easy it was to revert back to the old way of thinking and she guessed that is what happened upstairs. She decided to wait her mother out, to see if she could figure it out on her own.

It did not take long.

"What have I done?" Christine moaned, mentally clubbing herself for falling back into the trap of self-loathing, guilt and hatred.

Savanna started giggling, which quickly burst into full blown laughter. Her mother's reaction was not pretty. Before her mother could chastise her for laughing, Savanna said quickly, "Think about what you are doing right now."

Christine looked startled and then decided to let Savanna help her. She closed he eyes and mentally took a step back from her emotions. She became the observer and saw in an instant what went wrong with her husband.

"Oh no!" she cried in dismay. "I went back into guilt and that forced him away." She started crying softly, certain that she would never learn how to remain calm and peaceful in the midst of her daily struggles.

Savanna refused to be drawn into her mother's misery. She swung her legs around the side of the chaise lounge and faced her mother squarely. Her blue eyes were focused intently on this person whom she loved more than anyone in the world. But instead of being the child, at this moment, Savanna became the parent.

She lightly touched her mother's arm, sending waves of love to her. Christine jumped as the jolt of energy flowed through her. Before she could process what was happening, Savanna asked again.

"Think about what you are doing *right* now."

Savanna's tone carried such strength of conviction that it startled Christine. She sat still for another few minutes and then it hit her.

She was judging herself... for judging herself!

Laughter spilled out of her mouth before her hand tried to stop the flow. She glanced over at Savanna and they both started laughing together. It took a few minutes before they regained control enough to talk.

"Oh honey," Christine choked out between breaths. "I had no idea that I was doing that!"

Savanna nodded in understanding. "I don't think you have had enough time to figure out how to remember what you learned in the park. I had an entire week to work it out in my head."

Christine smiled at this lovely young woman who was quickly becoming more of a dear friend than a daughter she had to protect. The truth of Savanna's words resonated with her and she fell back into the deep cushions. After several minutes of peaceful silence, a startling thought made Christine sit up suddenly.

"What did you do when you touched my arm just now?"

Savanna knowing smile gave her away. "Didn't that also happen in your dream?"

"Whatever you did, it felt the same as when..." Christine paused as she made the connection. Both times, when she was in the throes of guilt, anger and despair, the energy shot she received from a gentle loving touch seemed to blow away the veil of her defenses. It was only after that touch that she could actually see, without being caught in the emotion, what she was doing to herself.

Savanna waited patiently while her mother considered all of the possibilities. She expected her mother to ask more questions about whom she learned that technique from, or how could she know how to do that. Instead, Christine's next question surprised her.

"Can you teach me how to do that?"

Savanna laughed in delight and jumped up from the chair and grabbed her mother's hands, pulling her to her feet. Savanna's eyes danced with anticipation as she exclaimed, "I'm just a student, but I know exactly the person to teach you!"

Christine laughed at her daughter's exuberance and nodded in agreement. She knew that Savanna understood the amazing transformation that had taken place in her heart. Christine felt overwhelmed with gratitude and love for this wonderful person who stood in front of her. She smiled at her daughter, amazed that Savanna was showing her the way.

Christine pulled Savanna into her arms for a fierce, all-consuming hug of love. They swayed together in peace and harmony, until their feet began moving to a different beat. The adult and almost adult-child danced around the deck, holding hands and laughing. When they were tired and sweaty, they fell back laughing on the chaise, breathing hard.

"I feel so different," cried Christine, throwing her arms out wide. Her right hand almost hit Savanna's face, which caused another round of joyous laughter. They sat, their legs and torso leaning on each other, catching their breath.

After their hearts had returned to a normal rhythm and their breathing slowed, Savanna glanced at her mother and asked playfully, "Do you want to meet your new teacher?"

Christine looked at her with question marks in her eyes, but she was willing to go along with anything. This day had been extraordinary enough – why not add one more adventure?

Savanna was already rushing out the front door. She called over her shoulder as she pulled her bike from the garage, "Come on!"

Christine laughed and shook her head. She took the time to get her keys, wallet and cell phone, locked the door and walked slowly toward her daughter.

"Where are we going?" she asked gently.

Savanna laughed as she began to pedal. "You are going to love this!" she cried happily.

Christine sighed and got on her bike. "You know I don't like surprises, Savanna!"

"You're going to love this one," she called over her shoulder as she rode into the street toward the park.

Christine had no choice but to follow. She decided to enjoy the experience and go with the flow, something she rarely allowed herself to do. She felt free for the first time in years, and as she pedaled her bike, Christine knew that she had just stepped back into her life.

When they arrived at the park, Christine expected Savanna to stop by their tree. Instead, she kept going up the hill and down the other side, away from the duck pond.

"Where are you going, young lady?" Christine felt compelled to ask in an authoritative tone.

"Mom, it's O.K. I've been this way before," Savanna called back.

Christine was about to chastise her daughter for riding beyond her set boundaries when she realized that it would ruin their joyful mood. She deliberately chose another response, which was to say nothing. Christine could almost hear her "spiritual self" say, "Alright – great job!" and she smiled to herself.

They continued to ride to a different part of town, one that was more out in the country. Christine looked around in amazement and realized that she had never bothered to explore this area before. The dirt road they were on seemed to lose itself in the forest, and the stately pine trees formed a canopy over their heads. They left the sunlight behind and were now in a world of brown, green and gray.

"Where are we?" she called to her daughter, who was still pedaling much faster.

Savanna slowed down enough to call back, "We're almost there." She braked her bicycle so hard that the back tires skidded slightly to the right. "Wait a minute – I just remembered something!" she said to her mother, who had just pulled up and stopped.

Christine was glad for the rest and took a minute to drink some cool, fresh water from her travel bottle. She offered some to Savanna, but she waived it off distractedly.

"I know I am in the right place," Savanna muttered to herself, as she looked into the deep forest for clues.

"You mean you don't know where we're going?" Christine asked in surprise.

Savanna heard the slight distress in her mother's voice and stopped searching long enough to stare deeply into Christine's eyes. "We're fine, mother," she said quietly, with a hint of authority.

Just then, they heard the faint barking of a dog, coming from behind them. Savanna jumped off from her bike and ran over to face that side of the road. As she slowly walked over and faced the forest, a mailbox materialized in front of her.

Savanna smiled to herself and waived her mother over. "See – I told you we were in the right place!" she cried.

Christine walked over to the mailbox and looked at it more closely. "That's amazing," she said to herself. "Look at the detail!"

Savanna looked at the mailbox and saw the same intricate detail. The yellow house, with the red door and the tiny rocking chairs on the porch.

"Wait a minute," Savanna muttered.

Instead of two rocking chairs on the porch like the last time she had seen it, now there were four!

"I wonder what that means," she muttered more to herself than to her mother.

Christine looked at her daughter closely. "What is different now than before?"

Savanna laughed sheepishly and answered, "The last time I was here, there were only two rocking chairs on the porch," she explained. "Now there are four."

Christine puzzled over that information for a moment, and then asked, "What do these initials mean?" The letters "DWTD" were still painted on the roof of the mailbox.

Savanna shrugged nonchalantly and suggested, "Maybe that stands for the name of the person who lives here."

Christine took a deep breath and said, more to herself than to her daughter, "I guess all of these mysteries will be revealed in their own good time."

Savanna nodded her agreement. "At least now I know we are at the right place," she said with excitement. She closed her eyes and took a deep breath, releasing the tension in her shoulders and neck. Christine was about to ask what she was doing, when an amazing thing happened.

A narrow driveway opened up in the woods! It was almost as if Savanna had rung an invisible doorbell and the driveway was the door that opened in response. Christine looked at her daughter in astonishment, but Savanna remained completely focused on the narrow dirt road that wound through the dense forest, waiting for someone to appear.

It did not take long.

Obscured by the trees and the shadows, Christine could see something moving about 50 feet away from them, but she could not tell who or what it was. She held her breath and waited with a shiver of anticipation. The forms moved closer until she recognized them. A gasp formed in her throat just as Savanna bolted down the drive toward the figures.

It was Avery and Avatar!

Savanna and Avatar danced around each other, laughing and barking while Avery stood very still, her eyes locked on Christine. Christine stood in shock for the span of several heartbeats, then her face broke out into a grin and she ran down the driveway toward her future.

A shaft of brilliant sunlight shone through the dense foliage like a spotlight on Avery. As Christine drew closer, she stopped in mid-stride, caught by the beauty of the moment. Avery's small face and body seemed lit from within, almost as if she were transparent. Savanna and Avatar sensed the change in the atmosphere and they stopped playing to watch.

Christine stood just outside the puddle of light, watching Avery closely. Avery smiled once at her then did the most astonishing thing – she began to waltz slowly in the light circle. As she gracefully moved around the driveway, the spot of light actually followed her! When the circle of light gently touched Christine's feet, she knew that she had just received her invitation to join the dance.

Christine glanced over at Savanna, who nodded her encouragement. The love that shone in her daughter's eyes gave her the courage to step into the circle. Christine smiled at Avery and took her hand. And then, they danced.

It was if time stood still, the earth stopped spinning for a brief instant as the world held its breath. The celebration of a new soul, finally awake to her Divine nature, made the angels smile. All-consuming love glowed between and around them, and their connection to God became tangible. Hearts danced together to an infinite song of love.

Christine felt her small self...dissolve into nothingness. A shimmering being, full of light and love, stepped forward in her place. Her mind could not accept what was happening; so it shut down to protect itself. But her heart knew – and it overflowed with love and gratitude. As she looked into Avery's eyes, she caught a glimpse of eternity, and she knew her life had forever changed.

She had just danced with the Divine!

13

A Lesson in Thought Training

To dance is to be out of yourself.
Larger, more beautiful, more powerful.
~Agnes De Mille

A short while later, Christine and Savanna had tea with Avery in her small house in the woods. As they sat together in the cozy living room, the windows open to catch the afternoon breeze, the sound of tires on the dirt road broke the silence. Avery smiled to herself as Christine and Savanna looked at each other in surprise. This cabin was remote and difficult to find, how could anyone else know about it?

As Avery opened the door to welcome the visitor, Christine and Savanna stood. When they saw who it was, they both gasped in astonishment.

It was Janet Andersen, Savanna's principal!

Christine was the first to recover. "Janet," she cried. "How do you know Avery?"

Ms. Andersen pulled Avery next to her in a loving hug, smiled, and said, "Look closely and you will see the answer."

Christine and Savanna looked back and forth between the two faces. Savanna was the first to figure it out. "You're her mother!" she said excitedly. A thoughtful look passed over her face. "Now I understand why you didn't mind that I was meeting Avery in the park – because you're her mother!"

It was Christine's turn to speak. "Janet, I always you knew you had a grown daughter, but I thought she lived in California with her father."

Ms. Andersen motioned for the group to return to the sofa and after everyone had settled, she began, "That's true. Avery did live in California with her father. But she came back here in January to continue her studies."

"What studies?" Christine asked in confusion.

Avery and her mother shared a knowing look, before Avery turned back to Christine. "I am studying to become a Teacher of God," she declared softly.

Now it was Savanna's turn to look confused. "What do you teach?" she asked. "And why do you teach it?" she added as the thought occurred to her.

Both Ms. Andersen and her daughter laughed at the simple innocence of Savanna's questions. Avatar came in from the small kitchen, tail waiving freely and a big doggy grin on his face. He seemed to join in the laughter and added his own contribution with a small bark.

By this time, Savanna and Christine were smiling too, but their faces betrayed their thoughts. "We don't get it," Christine finally admitted.

Ms. Andersen smiled and took Christine's slender hand in her own. "I know, dear. Sorry, but Avery and I always share that as a private joke." She paused, and then continued. "We didn't mean any harm."

Avery took over the conversation and looked directly at Savanna. "Remember when I asked you to answer my question?"

Savanna nodded slowly. She turned to her mother to explain. "When I first met Avery, I was very angry and upset about Dad..." Her head hung low as she remembered the pain of those days that seemed so long ago. "I was angry at the world, and that is why I cheated on the test. It just didn't seem to make any difference."

Both Christine and Ms. Andersen nodded as they also remembered those dark days. Christine was the first to speak. "So how did you meet Avery?"

"I rode to the park and fell asleep by the duck pond." Before she could continue, Christine interrupted to ask, "You mean in the same aspen grove where I feel asleep?"

Savanna nodded and then the light of understanding dawned in her eyes. "There must be something about that spot..." she began excitedly. But Avery stopped her in mid-sentence with her hand held up in the universal sign of "Stop." Savanna's mouth dropped open in surprise, as Avery stood up.

"What happened to both of you was the result of your Higher Self, not because you fell asleep in the same place," she declared with authority.

Ms. Andersen smiled kindly and said to both of the Hartts, "This is a touchy subject with Avery, as you can see."

Christine Hartt nodded in agreement. She turned to Savanna and said gently, "Let's respect Avery's wishes, honey. Go ahead with your story."

Savanna looked confused but she was willing to trust her mother's instincts. She took a deep, cleansing breath and continued.

"When I woke up, I saw something move. I hid behind the tree until I could get a better look." She paused for effect then said, "When I saw Avery and Avatar walking away from me, I decided to follow them." A new thought entered her mind. She turned to Avery and asked, "How did you guys get away from me so easily that first time?"

Avery laughed and said, "That is part of becoming a Teacher." She paused and added gently, "You are not yet ready to hear that explanation."

Savanna was about to ask why when her mother lightly touched her arm. Christine shook her head and then motioned for Savanna to continue with her story. Savanna sighed heavily, as only a teenager can do, and continued.

"I kept trying to catch them, but I never could." She paused, remembering how she was finally able to meet Avery and her dog. "It wasn't until I stopped chasing them and just asked for them to show up, that they did."

Avery and her mother nodded. Ms. Andersen said, "You can't chase yourself by focusing on what is happening outside of you. You have to go within."

Avery looked closely at Savanna, and then prompted her, "What was the first question I asked you when we finally met in person?"

Savanna was lost in her memories. When she heard Avery's question, she came back to the room. She looked back at Avery with pure love written in her eyes. "You wanted to know why it took me so long," she replied softly.

Avery nodded at her student. "And what was your answer?"

Savanna stood up with joy on her face. "I had to wake up!" she almost shouted, her voice filling the small room and floating out the windows to the forest beyond.

Avery stood in front of Savanna and looked deep into her eyes. They both smiled in recognition and gave each other a full body hug of appreciation.

Christine Hartt sat in total silence as she digested these events. She finally turned to Ms. Andersen and asked, "What did she have to wake up from?"

Ms. Andersen motioned for Savanna to sit back down. "I think I will let Avery answer that question," she said kindly.

Avery pulled away from Savanna and slowly turned toward Christine. Silence filled the small house as Christine looked deeply into Avery's eyes, and saw her answer.

Divine Love.

Christine gasped and pulled away from the intimate contact with Avery. "How did you do that?" she cried in distress.

Savanna sat down next to her mother and took her hand. "What happened?" she asked in concern.

Christine looked like she was in shock. She continued to stare at Avery as if she were an alien creature who just appeared in the middle of the tiny living room. She sat, frozen in shock, a dazed look in her eyes. Her breathing was shallow and her face was pale white. Savanna squeezed her mother's hand in concern and looked up at Ms. Andersen for help.

"Avery, why don't you get Christine some water," Ms. Andersen directed.

Avery nodded and smiled to herself as she stepped into the kitchen. She knew exactly what had just happened to Christine, but she had to allow Christine the time to process it. Avery hummed to herself as she made a plate of cheese, crackers and fruit. She arranged everything in a pleasing pattern on the plate, and carried it, along with a pitcher of frosty lemonade and glasses back out to the living room.

Avery continued to hum while she set up the food and drinks. When she poured a glass of lemonade and stood in front of Christine, Christine seemed to return to herself. She rose gingerly, as if her body was not working properly. Christine took the glass gently from Avery's hand, and set it on the coffee table. She took both of Avery's slender hands in her own, and looked deeply into Avery's eyes.

"Thank you," she said softly, as Avery's face lit up with joy. They hugged each other for several minutes while Savanna and Ms. Andersen walked outside to give them some privacy.

They sat down in the rocking chairs and waited. As Savanna allowed the peace of the forest to infuse her spirit, she smiled and began rocking gently. After several moments, she noticed that there were two empty chairs on the porch.

"Wait a minute," she said to herself, a puzzled look on her face.

She looked back at the house and saw that it was painted the same sunny yellow as the mailbox, with the same candy apple red front door. The only thing she could not confirm from her cursory examination was whether there were any initials painted on the roof.

Savanna turned toward Ms. Andersen and asked, "Did Avery know we were coming?"

Ms. Andersen nodded slightly and smiled. "That is part of becoming a Teacher," she explained. "Avery has learned to listen to her spiritual self."

Savanna nodded, but was still puzzled. "What is the spiritual self?"

"It is that part of you that is always connected to God." Ms. Andersen looked closely at Savanna to make sure she understood the explanation.

Savanna nodded. "I am starting to understand." She looked thoughtfully at the trees and then continued. "But I still have questions."

"Let me see if I can help," Ms. Andersen responded kindly. She added quickly, "But I am not a trained Teacher, so Avery will probably need to step in when I don't know the answer."

Savanna nodded. "That's O.K. Here is my first question. When do we get our spiritual selves?"

Ms. Andersen nodded and said, "That is as good a place to start as any." She looked at Savanna and saw only respectful attentiveness in her eyes. "When we are born on this planet, it is our spiritual selves slowing down to become part of the physical body."

Savanna shook her head because she did not understand. "What do you mean, 'slowing down' and where do the spiritual selves come from?"

A small smile played on Ms. Andersen's lips as she considered Savanna's questions. "You're right," she replied. "I really did not start at the beginning, did I?"

Savanna shook her head and smiled in return.

Ms. Andersen continued the lesson. "Your spiritual self is that part of you that is always connected to God." Ms. Andersen waited for that message to sink in before she asked, "Since your spiritual self is always connected to God, where do you suppose your spiritual self came from before she arrived on the earth to become the physical you?"

Savanna did not hesitate. "She came from God."

"Exactly!" Ms. Andersen cried proudly.

When she did not continue, Savanna prompted her by asking, "But what did you mean about 'slowing down'?"

Ms. Andersen nodded. "When your spiritual self is with God, she is vibrating at a very high frequency. Her energy is the same as God's, if you can imagine that!"

Savanna nodded and smiled. "So when my spiritual self decided to come to earth, she had to slow down enough to become physical?"

"You are a bright one, aren't you?"

Savanna ducked her head in embarrassment at the compliment. After a brief moment, she returned with more questions.

"Something has always bothered me, Ms. Andersen."

"What is it, dear?"

"That first day in your office, after I punched Jack, you said something to me that I am still trying to figure out." Savanna looked at Ms. Andersen and continued. "You told me that when I ask a 'why' question, that was the wrong question to ask." Savanna paused, and then asked slowly, a glint of humor in her tone at the irony of her next inquiry.

"But why is 'why' the wrong question?"

Ms. Andersen chuckled then took Savanna's hand. "I knew you were listening that day! You just were not ready to hear the answer. That is why I decided to let you work it out for yourself."

A look of frustration clouded Savanna's features. "But I still don't get it!" she cried a little too loudly. A crow that had been napping in one of the pine trees flew off with a loud caw at the sudden explosion of noise. It made both women jump slightly in their rockers. They laughed and settled back into their conversation.

"I obviously haven't figured it out," Savanna said sheepishly, nodding at the place where the crow had been.

Ms. Andersen nodded and smiled. "Things take time, Savanna. Be gentle with yourself. You are unlearning a lot of things that you thought you knew."

Companionable silence filled the space between them. Savanna thought over her recent conversation with her mother about the wrongness of 'why' questions and suddenly, the answer was clear.

"I've got it!" she exclaimed.

Ms. Andersen waited patiently, while Savanna burst out, "When I ask 'why' questions, I stay stuck in my story. I shut God out and can't hear his answer!"

Ms. Andersen reached over and gave Savanna a quick hug. "Well done!" Ms. Andersen smiled and asked gently, "Do you know how your 'story' is created?"

"It has something to do with my thoughts..." Savanna said tentatively.

"Correct. But who chooses your thoughts?" Ms. Andersen asked gently.

Savanna thought for a moment, and then said, "I used to think I had no control over my thoughts, but I now know that I do. So I must be the one to choose what I am thinking about." She glanced shyly at her mentor for an indication that she was on the right track.

"Good," Ms. Andersen said with approval. "So how do you create your story if you are the only one to choose what you think about?"

"I guess I create my story from my thoughts," Savanna ventured as a question and a statement.

Ms. Andersen hugged her student. "Good!" She paused for effect. "Now, if you create your story from the thoughts you choose to think, how can you change your story?"

Savanna thought about the question and suddenly the answer hit her over the head. "I just change my thinking and my story will have to change!" she cried exuberantly.

"Exactly," Ms. Andersen nodded her approval. "What happens when your story makes you sad, or depressed or angry?"

Savanna did not hesitate. "I start spiraling down into the vortex," she said with a twinkle in her eye.

Ms. Andersen looked startled at the analogy. "What is a vortex?"

"Haven't you ever been to the water park?" Savanna asked. "There is a ride called 'The Vortex.' You ride a tube inside a giant funnel. You start at the top, going 'round and 'round, until you start to lose momentum and you slide into the hole, through a dark tunnel and out the chute." She grinned at the thrilling memories. "It's awesome!"

Ms. Andersen shook her head. "Well, if you see that when you hold onto a story that makes you go deeper into the negative emotions the story generates, then that is a good analogy." She stopped for a moment while considered something. "Actually, I had a different analogy in mind."

Savanna decided to be the good student, and she asked sincerely, "What is it?"

"Imagine that you have a pair of special sunglasses," Ms. Andersen began. "You get to choose the color of the lenses by your thoughts.   Red for anger, blue for depression..."

"Yellow for joy?"

"Yes, that's right. Now, the lenses change instantly when you change your story. But whatever you think about, you will see it happen through the filter of the lenses."

Savanna considered the image that she saw in her mind. "So if I think my friends are mad at me, I will see them through that lens?"

Ms. Andersen nodded. "Yes, that's right. And you decide every second what you are going to see in every moment."

"So to change the lens and see something different, I just change my thoughts about it?"

"Correct."

Savanna looked up at the towering pines that ringed the cabin, dancing in the wind. She allowed her thoughts to drift and she thought about her mother, struggling to give up her story. "Why did it take so long for my mother to give up her story?"

Ms. Andersen smiled gently. "Everyone is on their own journey through life, Savanna. Please don't judge your mother for her own path. She reached the place where she could let go of her story when it was the best time for her." She shook her head and glanced at the ground. "That is really between your mother and God," she finally added.

Savanna was not quite ready to give up. "But she kept it going for years and years!"

Ms. Andersen took Savanna's hands into her own and gave a loving squeeze. "Can't you see how powerful your thoughts are?" she asked earnestly. "Your mother was caught in her own vortex of anger, guilt, shame and frustration. And she looked through her life with those beliefs filtering her experience."

Savanna nodded in understanding. She recalled how fiercely her mother defended her actions about the baby and the reasons why she took such a drastic step. No amount of debate, discussion or understanding could change her mind.

"Your mother had to forgive and release herself from her past decisions before she could heal."

The younger woman looked at her mentor and friend with new eyes of appreciation. "I can see that now – because my mother was punishing herself for her past, she wasn't free to live in the present." Savanna glanced upwards at the top of the pine trees dancing in the wind. She added thoughtfully, "Her past clouded the present, didn't it?"

Ms. Andersen nodded, more at the accepting tone of Savanna question, than at its contents. She waited a few minutes for Savanna to digest this new information. Then she added, "Just remember – God supports you no matter what you do."

"What do you mean?"

"Remember when I told you that you are really a spiritual being having a physical experience?"

Savanna nodded. "I had to slow way down to get inside this body," she said playfully.

"Right," Ms. Andersen acknowledged. "Well, when you choose thoughts from your spiritual self, you will grow and expand. When you chose thoughts from your ego, you withdraw and diminish." She paused, looking for the right words. "And no matter what thoughts you choose, God will support you."

Savanna shook her head. "I don't get it!"

"When you were mad at your parents, how did you act? Big or small?"

The question made Savanna pause. She thought about getting into the fight with Jack, then cheating on her test. "I guess I acted small," she whispered.

"And after you met Avery and Avatar, how did you act?"

Savanna glanced up at her mentor and saw only love and admiration. There was no judgment or condemnation, which gave Savanna the courage to declare, "I acted much bigger than I was."

Ms. Andersen hugged her again. "Exactly! And God supported you in both situations. It's totally up to you to choose whether you want to play small and fearful or expand with love to become as big a person as you can."

"You mean that love expands and fear contracts?"

"That's it. And it always works, no matter how much you want it to work differently." Ms. Andersen paused as she considered her next words. "Can't you see now that your thoughts control your reality?" She held her breath, hoping that her student would take this last step toward freedom.

It didn't take long. Savanna nodded and smiled as she agreed, "I am going to have to experiment with that theory...but it will be fun to see that when I change my thoughts about something, it also changes what I see." She paused as she thought back over the last week. "Wait a minute – I have already done that!"

Ms. Andersen knew that Savanna was working out these principles in her own mind, so she sat silently, waiting on Savanna to describe what she just remembered.

It didn't take long.

Savanna turned excitedly towards the older woman. "After I finally met Avery and we talked, she touched my arm and then I knew...the next day when I went to school, I felt like I was watching everyone from a different place. My thoughts about them had changed and I could actually see the fear behind their games."

Ms. Andersen nodded in approval. "Once you have experienced who you truly are, you will have a hard time going back to playing small." She smiled at her pupil and added, "You have to be mindful of your thoughts, though, because the events of the world can pull you back into fear."

"What do I do if that happens?"

"Tell yourself that you are a Child of God and you know you are worthy."

"That's it?" Savanna was slightly taken aback by this simple advice.

Ms. Andersen nodded and smiled, opening her palms to receive and closing her eyes. She breathed in deeply and after a moment, seemed to glow from within. When she opened her eyes again, the love light shone like a laser.

Savanna accepted the love offering and smiled joyously. They hugged and swayed in this shared knowledge of their Divine connection.

After a few moments, Savanna felt compelled to ask her mentor another question.

"How did you do that so easily? It always takes me a lot longer..."

Ms. Andersen laughed and teasingly said, "It's not a competition to see who comes in first, Savanna. Just like anything, you have to practice. I have been practicing every day for years, so I know exactly how to plug in."

Savanna thought for a moment before asking, "So the connection is always there, but it's up to me to open the way?"

"Yes – that's it. God is always there - waiting to be connected to you – but you have to say 'yes' before the love can flow to you and through you."

"So when I feel myself slipping into fear, all I have to do is take a minute, breathe deeply and ask for God's help?"

Ms. Andersen nodded in agreement. She looked around the forest and noticed the birds flitting among the branches and the leaves on the pine trees filtering the sunlight. She thoughtfully added another observation, gesturing to the living things around her to make her point. "When you know that you are always connected to God, why would you ever choose to be dis-connected?"

Savanna took a deep breath and absorbed the life that went about their business without worrying about what the next day might bring. She thought about what her mentor was trying to say. Finally, a new thought came to her and tentatively, she said, "It's almost as if I have two of 'me.' The 'me' I thought I knew, and the 'spiritual me.' Am I on the right track?"

"Well done, my dear!" Ms. Andersen cried with enthusiasm.

"You mean I am right about having two of 'me'?"

"You are absolutely right!" Ms. Andersen paused. "The 'you' that you think is the real you is only a creation of your ego. Let's call it the 'ego-you.' The other 'you' – can you guess what that is?"

Savanna nodded happily. "It's my 'spiritual-me.'"

"Right! So can you see how the 'ego-you' can totally cover up your 'spiritual-you'?"

Savanna sat for a moment and thought about everything that had happened to her in the last week. The light of understanding shone from her sky blue eyes as a new realization hit her.

"Now I get it!" she cried in excitement. "When I live only from my 'ego-me' I ask 'why' questions." Savanna knew she was on the right track and waited impatiently for confirmation.

Ms. Andersen did not disappoint her. "Savanna, you are amazing!" she declared proudly. Savanna basked in her praise and smiled happily. Ms. Andersen smiled at her new spiritual student and continued.

"The quality of your life depends on the type of questions you ask," Ms. Andersen announced with conviction. She waited to see if Savanna would follow that statement to its obvious conclusion.

Savanna tentatively asked, "So 'why' questions are from the 'ego-me'?"

"Exactly!" Ms. Andersen nodded in approval. "See if you can work out the rest of it," she prodded gently

"Well, if 'why' questions are from the 'ego-me,' then what kind of questions does the 'spiritual-me' ask?" Savanna was eager to hear the answer, and she stopped rocking and leaned forward intently.

Ms. Andersen smiled and answered, "What kind of questions expand you and make you feel good about yourself and others?"

Savanna sighed and leaned back in the chair. She began rocking again while her mind worked to solve the puzzle. She thought about the last week and the moments when she had felt completely and totally happy. Her mind glided over the events that surrounded that happiness, and then she realized the connection.

"I don't know the right way to put this..." Savanna glanced at Ms. Andersen, who nodded encouragingly. "But when I focused on listening to God and not my ego-self, I seemed to expand beyond my physical body."

Ms. Andersen gently placed Savanna's hand in between her two larger ones. "And what type of question keeps you focused on listening to God instead of yourself?"

Savanna shook her head in frustration. She took a deep breath and let the peacefulness of the forest, this gentle woman and the moment invade her soul. Instead of trying to please Ms. Andersen, Savanna relaxed and just allowed herself to be in the moment. Intense joy burst through from her very spirit when she realized the answer.

Savanna put her other hand on top of Ms. Andersen's, looked her straight in the eyes, and said with conviction, "When I ask 'what would love do now?' or 'how can I serve,' my focus is on God!"

Ms. Andersen grabbed the younger woman in a warm embrace and rocked her gently. Mere words could not describe this moment of shared truth, because it was too charged with vibrant energy. Savanna relaxed in the older woman's arms and felt true love fill up every cell of her body. She knew she would never be the same again, and she felt intense gratitude well up inside of her.

"Thank you so much," Savanna's whisper was for one set of ears, but her spiritual-self celebrated by dancing within. Tears of joy ran down both their faces.

Ms. Andersen was the first to break out of the embrace. "Well," she began as she wiped her eyes to clear the tears. "Do you think we should check on them?"

Savanna nodded and ran a hand over her face as well. As she stood up and stretched, a sudden thought occurred to her. "Ms. Andersen, you said you were not a Teacher." Savanna paused with a mischievous glint in her eyes. "But I think you just proved yourself wrong!"

The older woman laughed and gave Savanna a friendly hug. "It's not up to me to decide, but thank you for your vote of confidence!"

Just as Savanna was about to ask who decides when you become a Teacher, the front door opened and her mom stepped over the threshold. Avery was just behind her. Ms. Andersen and Avery looked deeply into each other's eyes, and they shared much in their silent exchange.

Christine walked over to her daughter, and they hugged fiercely. After a brief tick of time, they said their goodbyes and walked over to their bicycles. Savanna did not say a word while they rode down the dirt driveway dappled in late afternoon sunlight, away from the little house in the woods. Two figures stood on the porch and waved good-bye.

Just as they were about to disappear into the dark shadows of the forest, Avatar burst from the house and bounded after them, barking happily. Savanna and Christine glanced at each other, startled at the sudden noise, but they stopped their bicycles and twisted around to look behind them. Savanna jumped off her bike and ran to meet the golden dog, his long tail waiving furiously like a banner.

Doggy kisses and happy hugs engulfed her. Christine set her bike down more slowly and walked up to the big dog, respectfully waiting for him to finish saying goodbye to Savanna.

After a few minutes, Avatar pulled away from Savanna and sat down in front of Christine. She recognized the dignified invitation and knelt down so she could look into his face. She began to pet him as his tongue hung long and low outside his large mouth, grinning happily. Christine was about to stand up when she noticed something that took her breath away.

Love Divine was shining bright and true in Avatar's eyes!

Christine's heart broke open completely. All of her defenses, pretenses and stories disappeared into the thinning light. When she stood apart from them, she saw them for exactly what they were.

They were only illusions, with no substance, no basis and no truth.

Another startling realization hit her between her heart and her solar plexus. It took her breath away and she was completely open to inspiration and guidance. It was so simple, yet so profound.

Pure and complete love was always there for her – it was only because she chose to believe in her stories that the love became invisible!

This stunning insight was like an arrow, shot straight through her ego-self and pinning it in the red center of the target. Instantly, she saw the world that she created when she listened to her ego. Pain, doubt, humiliation, shame, guilt and frustration were the start of a long list of complaints and unhappiness. It all circled in on itself and created a complex maze with no exit.

It was a vortex of no hope, no love...for herself or those around her.

And definitely, no room for God.

Now that she could see the consequences of following her ego, she knew that she would never fall into that snare again. Her eyes closed in silent prayer and thanksgiving, gratitude spilling over and flowing from her. It was Avatar's warm tongue on her face, licking her in approval that brought her back to the moment.

Christine laughed joyously and hugged the dog, his soft fur tickling her face. She whispered in his ear, "Thank you for your gift," before pulling away and gently gathering his face in her hands. She took a moment to shine her new love awareness back to him in gratitude.

Avatar accepted the accolades as his reward. He knew the truth about God, so why was it so hard for these people to get it? He never questioned why he was here or what his purpose was. He knew, simply and completely, that he was supposed to love freely, without reservation or hesitation. And in passing on God's love to everyone else, God's love flowed through him. It was that simple.

Christine kissed Avatar's long nose and ruffled his ears one last time. Just as she was about to stand up, she glanced back at the dog and caught a surprise.

He actually winked at her!

Her startled look turned into laughter as she realized the truth. She now knew the secret to a happy life. Christine turned to Savanna and hugged her tightly, allowing love to flow freely to her daughter. She turned and waved again at Ms. Andersen and Avery, still standing on the front porch watching the entire scene play out in the driveway.

Savanna knew another seismic shift had occurred for her mother, but she did not want to press it just then. She decided to wait until they were back on the main road to ask questions.

After the bicyclists had disappeared, Janet turned to her daughter. They both said the words they had been thinking, at the same time.

"I love it when that happens!"

They turned to go inside the small house and being preparing dinner. Avatar was nosing around in the woods and scratched at the door several minutes later to be let inside. Avery squatted down in front of her dog and hugged him fiercely.

"Thank you again for your help, big guy," she said playfully.

His answer was answer enough. The long tongue licked her once in acknowledgement and the wink sealed the deal. He had done his job and he had done it well.

"Good dog," she said warmly, getting up to return to the kitchen. He followed expectantly, knowing that a great dinner was about to be served.

14

Can the Student Become the Teacher?

Movement never lies. It is a barometer telling the state of the soul's weather.
~ Martha Graham

When they reached the main road, Savanna turned expectantly toward her mother, questions about to fall from her lips. Christine held up her hand and silently pleaded with Savanna to wait. They rode home in silence, the rhythmic sound of the rubber tires on hard pavement keeping them company.

When they arrived home, they put up their bikes and slowly walked inside. By this time, dusk had fallen and the house was growing dark, except for the kitchen light that glowed over the sink. Savanna flipped on the switch for the outdoor light and was about to close the door, when Bandelier bounded inside. Her loud meow startled them both.

Christine started to feed the cat, but she was still so dazed and confused that Savanna gently told her, "You need to go lie down for a few minutes."

Christine nodded and smiled ruefully. "I guess I'm setting a record for the number of naps taken in one day," she said. As she left the kitchen, she said in a whisper, "Don't tell your father," and winked.

Savanna nodded in happy agreement. Her mother never would have made that comment unless she was going to work it out with her dad. Savanna started humming to herself as she fed Bandelier and grabbed some cheese and crackers for herself.

It was all going to work out.

She puttered around the kitchen, watching the calico cat enjoy her meal. She thought about watching some television, but the thought of sitting in front of some mindless program made her slightly sick to her stomach. She saw with perfect clarity all of the time she had wasted in front of that box, relying on it to fill her head with ideas. Whenever she watched one of her shows, she felt hypnotized and removed from herself, accepting someone else's dream about how life was supposed to work.

She would not give away her awareness again. Not when it was so new, so utterly and completely tied with her newly discovered self.

Her Spiritual-Self.

A part of Savanna was shocked at these new insights. It tried to resist and demand attention, but she knew now what that voice was and knew enough to ignore it. Her ego-self would have to learn to take its proper place in her life, as a tool but not as the driver. She decided what the direction she wanted to go in her life, not her ego.

Savanna finished cleaning up the kitchen and then went upstairs to her room. She was filled with a sense of awe that God loved her so much that He showed Himself to her so willingly. It was difficult to completely grasp love of that magnitude. She stayed with those feelings as long as she could, but her mind chatter finally kicked in and the connection was lost.

Savanna slowly walked into her room and started getting ready for bed. As she took off her jeans, she felt the piece of paper that she had put in her pocket. She drew it out and looked at it again. She studied it more closely and saw the words that she had missed downstairs.

Please add #MiracleToken to your Tweet to let me know you received this message. Miracle Token – Universal Currency. @MiracleIncome www.MiracleIncome.com

The simple instructions to "let me know you received this message" seemed to resonate in her head, somehow spoken in a soft yet powerful voice that sounded like James Earle Jones. Savanna's logical mind could not decipher the mystery of who wrote the message and why they wanted to know it had been received. But her spiritual mind knew without a doubt.

Somehow, this small, insignificant piece of paper contained a Divine message.

She wondered again at the coincidence of events that must have taken place for this piece of paper to find its way into her mother's grocery bag, on the very day of her awakening. Savanna knew that much more was at work here than met the eye, and she knew just the person to ask about it.

Avery.

The thought of her mentor made her smile. She placed the note on her dresser, next to her watch and necklace so she would remember to show it to Avery tomorrow. Savanna finished changing for bed and after brushing her teeth, she knew that she could not go to sleep. She slowly walked into her bedroom, seeing it with fresh eyes. She opened the window a crack and a cool breeze filled the space, fluttering the purple curtains and making them dance. The motion reminded her of what happened in the forest and her mind suddenly flashed to an image of the intricate wooden "mail house" at the end of Avery's driveway.

"DWTD."

"Avery never did tell me what those initials meant," Savanna sighed to herself.

Savanna smiled as she remembered the wondrous feeling of being connected to light and love in the forest. In her mind's eye, she was once again dancing in that wondrous pool of light. As she swayed back and forth, eyes closed and palms raised to receive, Savanna knew she was healed and whole. Her sense of herself now included something much bigger, and she knew she had only to reach out to the Divine to reconnect.

Suddenly, she heard a loud knocking downstairs, as if someone were banging on the front door. Shocked from her worship, Savanna's heart started beating wildly and a burst of adrenaline rushed through her bloodstream. Hard, short breaths kept time with the pounding of her feet going down the stairs.

Just as she was about to open the door, a deep bark came from the other side.

Instantly, Savanna knew who it was standing on her front porch. As the door swung open, Avery and Avatar flung themselves into the house, both wild-eyed and frightened.

"Avery – what is it?" Savanna managed to cry before Avery could speak.

Avery shook her head and held up her hand as she sat down on the sofa. Avatar was not so quick to calm down, and he kept barking, the deafening sound echoing off the walls, almost as if he was foreshadowing events to come.

After several seconds, Avery looked up at Savanna, her green eyes tinged with a deep-seated fear.

Savanna could not stand it any longer. She stood over the distraught young woman and bending down slightly, took Avery's hands. After a small squeeze of encouragement, Savanna asked her sternly, "Tell me what happened – you're scaring me."

"It's my mom," Avery managed to say as she pulled her hands out of Savanna's grasp. Deep sobs filled the room as she covered her face with her hands. Avatar immediately sensed the change in atmosphere, and sat down next to his master, leaning against her to give what comfort he could.

"Tell me quickly so we can help her," Savanna cried desperately.

Avery took a deep breath to steady herself and said quickly, "After you guys left, we went inside to fix dinner. We had just sat down to eat..." She paused and pain was written in her strained expression. She tried again. "We had just said the blessing and started to eat, when..."

Savanna gently touched Avery's knee as encouragement. Her heart was beating too fast and images of dire events flashed across her mind.

Avery seemed to gather herself and she looked up into Savanna's eyes. Avery's concern about her mother and fear of what could happen cast clouds of doubt, making her green eyes go almost gray.

"She was fine one minute, and then when she stood up...she just passed out."

Savanna's look of alarm spurned Avery to finish the story. "As she fell, she hit her head on the edge of the table and it caused a large gash just above her eye." Avery paused as the pain of watching her mother fall and hurt herself rushed through her again. "I couldn't get her to wake up," she cried desperately. "And...there was so much blood!"

The statement hung in the room, waiting for acknowledgment. Savanna did not hesitate. She jumped into action and pulled Avery into a standing position. "We have to go get my mom," she cried and she commanded Avery up the stairs to her mother's bedroom.

But just as they were about to take the first step, Christine appeared at the top of the stairs. When she saw Avery and felt the emotional charge in the room, she flew down the steps and gathered Avery into her arms.

"I just had the worst dream about your mother," she cried in alarm.

Avery started crying again and it took several minutes to calm her down. Christine had her sit in the den and waited for her to gain control of herself. Avatar faithfully sat by her side, whining softly, his big head in his master's lap. Avery absentmindedly stroked his head, but he knew that her attention was not on him. He tried licking her hand, but she finally pushed him away and stood up.

"I am so sorry to be this emotional," Avery said with a tinge of embarrassment. "But this has never happened before..."

Christine started asking her questions about what happened, and when she learned that Janet might have a possible head injury, Christine's medial training took over. Her mind immediately started going over checklists of what they needed to bring with them to the small cabin. Car keys, cell phone and first aid kit. Check. Avery to tell her how to reach the cabin.

As Christine was running out the front door, she cried over her shoulder, "Come on! We can call EMS on the way!"

As soon as the words "EMS" came out of Christine's mouth, Avery stopped abruptly and cried, "No one can know about the cabin in the woods!"

Both Savanna and her mom turned around and looked at Avery in astonishment. "But your mother needs immediate medical help," Christine cried. "I can only do so much!"

A look of determination crossed over Avery's features. "No one finds out about the cabin," she declared fiercely.

Christine could tell that her young mentor was not going to budge on this issue, so she made the prudent choice and gathered everyone into the car. As she flew along the dark, silent streets of Newridge, street lights pooling small areas, she prayed with all of her ability that Janet Andersen would regain consciousness. Because of her job at the hospital, Christine knew better than anyone the devastating effects a head injury can have on a person's mental and physical capacities.

The urgency of the situation made Christine take chances with her driving. The wheels of her car screamed around the curves in the park to reach the other side, where the smaller road took them through the forest. Instead of peace and calm, the trees stood as silent sentinels, warning them of possible tragedy. The short car ride was spent in tense anticipation of what they might find at the cabin. Avatar sensed the atmosphere and whined softly.

When they reached the mailbox, the trees seemed impenetrable. Avery took a deep breath, closed her eyes and suddenly, the drive appeared beside the mailbox. Savanna shook her head and muttered to herself, "I love it when that happens!"

The car slowly made its way through the forest, the trees standing tall, immovable and watchful. As they reached the clearing, Janet's car was still parked in front of the small cabin, but it blocked their view of the front porch. They jumped out and ran toward the structure, not knowing what they would find. Avery opened the front door and they all walked inside, expecting the worse.

No one was there.

Christine looked more closely at the wooden floor in the kitchen. She could see the pool of blood at the edge of the small table, where Janet had fallen and laid on the floor. But something was strange...

After a heartbeat, Christine saw the smear of blood on the edge of the table, almost as if Janet had touched her head, gotten blood on her hands, and then used the table to support her as she stood up.

Christine was reconstructing the events in her mind, based on the physical evidence in front of her. Obviously, Janet had managed to pull herself upright, but where was she now? Savanna and Avery had already checked the bathroom and bedroom, but no one could find her.

"Where could she have gone?" wondered Christine, as she continued to look for clues.

She made her way to the front door and spotted another blood stain, this time on the inside of the door. "There!" she cried, pointing to it. "She must have gone outside!"

Everyone rushed outside onto the small front porch. The outside light cast a low glow, making it difficult to discern small details such as a blood trail. As Christine continued to look for clues, Savanna stepped back inside to look for a flashlight. She passed the kitchen table and took one look at the dark red spot and felt her stomach turn over. "I hope she's going to be O.K.," she thought to herself.

Savanna found a flashlight hanging on a hook by the back door. She decided to go out that way and circle around to the front of the cabin to look for clues. Just as she was rounding the corner, she literally bumped into Avery, knocking them both to the ground.

After disentangling each other, they stood upright, brushing off their clothes. Savanna sensed that Avery was afraid, and she grabbed her in a quick, supportive hug.

"Where could she be?" moaned Avery in Savanna's left ear, on the brink of losing her self-control.

They made their way to the front of the house and looked to Christine for assurance. She held up her hands in the timeless gesture of "What now" and continued to look around the clearing. "I can't believe that we can't find her," she said to herself, not wanting to upset Avery even more.

Just then, furious barking came from the other side of Janet's car. They rushed over and saw Avatar standing on his back legs, front paws resting on the driver's door.

The golden retriever was barking at something inside the car!

Christine ran over and looked inside. Janet was sitting behind the steering wheel, but she had passed out again and was slumped over on the front seat. That is why they didn't notice her inside the car when they first arrived. Christine tried to open the door, but it was locked.

"Avery – quick! Do you have another set of keys?"

A look of disbelief flew across Avery's normally placid expression. "She never gave me any keys, because I don't drive."

"We have to call EMS to get her out!"

Avery stood in shock as she realized that to save her mother, she would have to allow other people into her sacred space. She was not ready to share her cabin with strangers. The twin dilemma of her love for her mother versus her commitment to becoming a Teacher tore a hole in her heart.

Christine could see the physical effort of Avery's internal conflict, but her overriding concern was for treating Janet's wounds as quickly as possible. In her most soothing, bed-side, patient voice, she put her arm around Avery and gently said, "She needs help."

Avery nodded at the truth of the words, and knew that she would have to trust that this would all work out. She closed her eyes and took a deep breath, holding it and then releasing it slowly through her mouth. The tension in her shoulders and neck also released and the vise-grip of fear around her heart loosened. She smiled to herself and turned to Christine, her features again peaceful.

"Thank you, Christine," she said softly. "Please do whatever you feel is necessary to help my mother."

Christine gave Avery a quick hug to acknowledge her courage and pulled out her cell phone to place the call to EMS.

While Christine and Avery were standing at the driver's door, working out the logistics of getting the car door open, Savanna moved to the passenger side rear door. A thought startled her into action. "Maybe this door isn't locked," she thought, as she raised the handle.

It opened!

Both Christine and Avery heard the sweet sound of the car door opening and they turned to look. Savanna slipped inside reached into the front, hitting the unlock button.

Just then, Janet Andersen started moaning.

Christine jumped into action and flung open the driver's side door. She undid Janet's seat belt and laid her gently across the front seat, murmuring that it was going to be all right. The large and deep gash on her forehead bore angry testament to the trauma that Avery's mom had suffered from her fall.

While Christine was helping Janet, Savanna and Avatar walked over to join Avery, who was staring at her mother with a perplexed expression.

Before Savanna could ask her what was wrong, Avery closed her eyes, tilted back her head, and with open hands and an open heart, gave thanks.

After a few moments, Avery opened her eyes and turned toward Savanna and Avatar. She quickly hugged them both and walked back over to the car to see how her mother was doing.

Janet was sitting up in the driver's seat, head leaned back against the headrest, eyes closed. Christine applied a bandage to her laceration and was watching her carefully. Her color was returning to normal, but she still felt too weak to move.

Christine took a moment to give Avery an update on her mother's condition. "I want her to stay here until she feels a bit stronger, then she should go to the hospital."

Avery nodded and did not argue. She leaned inside the car to give her mother a gentle kiss. Janet smiled and lightly touched her daughter's face, then her hand dropped back heavily into her lap.

Avery and Savanna slowly walked away from the car. The night sounds of the wind kept them company as they stood at the edge of the clearing, looking back on the small cabin and the car that was lit by the small overhead bulb. Avatar followed slowly, worn out from all of the excitement.

Savanna knew that her mentor had faced a crisis and she waited patiently for Avery to begin the conversation. Avery seemed to have an internal conversation with herself and then finally reached a decision.

"I am sure that you are wondering how I could ever value keeping my home protected more than getting help for my mother."

Savanna nodded and smiled to let her know that she was not being judged or condemned. The two young women stood in quiet friendship while the moon began to show itself in the small gap of space at the top of the trees. They watched it for a few moments in peaceful companionship.

Avery finally broke the silence. "I learned a valuable lesson tonight."

Savanna's raised eyebrow asked the next logical question.

"I am a Teacher no matter what is happening around me."

The simple statement was not what Savanna expected to hear. The surprise showed on her face and she was about to respond, when Avery held up her hand to stop her.

"Do you understand what I mean when I say 'Teacher'?"

The question hung in the air, shimmering with deep intent. Savanna was aware of the significance of the question and wanted to give a thoughtful answer. She waited for something wise to bubble up in her brain, but after a few seconds, she gave up. Shaking her head that she did not know the answer, she glanced at Avery, an apologetic look on her face.

Avery smiled gently and said, "Savanna, do you know how well you did tonight?"

Savanna shook her head but her demeanor perked up at the praise.

"While I was in a panic, you were there to help me." Avery paused as she remembered the urgency of finding her mother. "And you and Avatar were the ones to discover where she was." At the sound of his name, Avatar's tail started bumping loudly on the ground, and Avery bent down to give him a quick hug.

"And your mother..." Avery stopped while the emotions of the evening flooded through her. She allowed them to well up and flow out, and after a few minutes, had regained control.

Savanna waited and finally prompted her mentor and friend to continue.

"What about my mother?"

Avery smiled and nodded toward the car. "She is such a caring woman and a well-trained professional."

Almost as if Christine knew they were talking about her, she stood up next to the car and motioned for them to come over. As they approached, she asked for their help in moving Janet out of the driver's seat and into the passenger side.

When Savanna asked why they weren't taking her into the cabin, Christine said, "Her gash is too deep for me to suture it here. Plus, I am concerned about her blood pressure." She paused and looked at Avery before continuing. "It is my professional opinion that she needs to go to the hospital."

Avery nodded in agreement. Christine mentioned the fact that they would probably want to keep Janet overnight for observation, and Avery went inside to pack a small bag of clothes and other necessities for herself and her mother.

When she came back out, Christine suggested that she drive Janet's car to the hospital. Savanna spontaneous suggestion of "But Mom, I have my learner's permit and I could..." was cut off by her mother with a look of "not now."

Savanna acknowledged the message and climbed into the back seat of Janet's car.

Christine walked around to the driver's side, followed by Avery. Christine had worked out the logistics of leaving her car at the cabin, and mentioned to Avery that she would get a ride back tomorrow to get her car.

Avery nodded distractedly as she started to get into the back seat. She sighed when she saw Avatar had already claimed his space and ordered him outside. The golden retriever was not going to budge and looked patiently at his master. His expression said it all. "Well, what are we waiting for?" Avery knew that she would not win that battle and she hoped that the hospital staff would understand.

Christine found Janet's car keys still in the ignition and they were soon as on their way to the hospital. Silence descended on them as they left the solace of the forest and drove into town toward the hospital. Fortunately, Janet was quickly evaluated and admitted and Christine and Savanna were soon on their way home.

The house looked the same as when they had left it in such a hurry only a few short hours before. It was just before midnight and they were both exhausted from the intense experience of finding and helping Janet.

Before closing up the house and going to bed, Christine walked into Savanna's room. "I was very proud of you tonight," she said with a smile. Savanna looked up in surprise from her book and her mother continued.

"You never panicked. You kept looking for a solution – and you and Avatar were the ones who found Janet and got the car opened!"

Savanna smiled and said, "I was pretty awesome, wasn't I?"

Christine laughed at the tone as much as the content of that declaration. Just as she was turning to leave, Savanna got out of bed and gave her a quick hug.

"What was that for?" Christine asked.

In a teasing tone, Savanna said, "Now it's my turn. Mom – you were amazing!"

Christine looked a bit surprised as Savanna continued with her praise. "You took charge of the situation and knew exactly what to do!"

"That's what I am trained for as a nurse, honey," Christine responded, as she deflected the praise.

Savanna looked deep into her mother's eyes, willing her to see her own value. After a moment, Christine smiled ruefully as she realized what she had done and quietly said, "Thank you."

Savanna nodded and hugged her mother good night. She fell asleep the instant the light was turned off and her head hit the pillow.

Christine was not so lucky.

The events of the evening passed through her mind again. Her thoughts kept returning to Avery's struggle about whether to let strangers come to the cabin to help her mother. She admired the younger woman's courage and wondered briefly what Avery did in her moment of taking a deep breath.

Then she knew.

Avery surrendered her fear to God. Instead of trying to control the outcome, she allowed God to manage it for her. And the answer was immediate, direct and undeniable. As soon as Avery surrendered her will to God, Savanna discovered that the back door was unlocked.

In that instant of surrender, Avery's fear was transformed into love.

Gratitude washed over Christine as she thought about everything that had happened to her. The life-changing dream in the park; her conversation with Avery inside the cabin; her ability to help during Janet's crisis.

She could now see a new life for herself. One that used her training and strengths to help others. And the joy found in committing herself fully and authentically to her intimate relationships with her family and dear friends.

By giving up her story about the baby, she was free to grow, explore and learn to love again.

"Not a bad trade," she thought to herself.

Not a bad trade at all.

15

The Lawyer Meets the Divine

Dance is the hidden language of the soul.
~ Martha Graham

As the house quieted and Christine made sure that everything was turned off, something kept bothering her. She knew that she had handled the situation with Avery and Janet well and she was fairly certain that Janet was going to be O.K.

But there was something else that happened earlier in the day that nagged at her. As she walked up the stairs to the master bedroom, she kept thinking about Brian and the earlier scene in this very room. She knew that she had reacted harshly to his loving gesture and she truly missed him. On impulse, she composed a text message that simply said, "So sorry for today. I am here if you want to talk." She paused before hitting the "send" key, knowing that she would have to accept it if he did not respond. She closed her eyes and asked God to quickly send an answer.

Just then, her phone dinged with a new message. Christine thought to herself, "That sure was fast," as she slid her finger over the face of her phone. The words on the screen made her heart jump for joy.

"I will be right over."

The silence of the house did nothing to hide the pounding of her heart. Hope surged through her, and she said another silent prayer for guidance. Then she went to get dressed and go downstairs to wait.

It did not take long. A car door closed and she flew to the front window to see if it were him. She felt like she was 19 again and waiting for Brian to pick her up at her dorm room for a date. She was nervous, excited and in love.

A soft knock on the door announced his arrival. She did not hesitate but opened the door and flew into his arms.

Brian was not sure what to expect when the door opened, but he absolutely did not, in a million years, expect his wife to fling herself into his arms. He did not have time to think but only time to react. His arms closed around her immediately and it felt like he had come home.

They hugged each other, enjoying the warm embrace and allowing the healing touch to mend their wounds. After some time, Christine pulled away and pulled him into the house. She was excited, happy and couldn't wait to share all of the events that had happened that day.

Brian was more cautious. He could see that she had changed, but he had made the mistake of believing the change was permanent this afternoon, and her rejection of his kiss still stung. Tonight, no matter what she said, he would remain a bit more aloof.

Of course, he already blew it as soon as he walked through the door.

Christine did not notice his reluctance immediately. She was too caught up in her exuberance at being able to share her newly discovered connection to the Divine and giving up her story. She pulled him into the den, had him sit down in their favorite spot on the sofa, and went to fix a snack of cheese, crackers, grapes and two glasses of Chardonnay.

Brian forgot about the small daypack that he had automatically slung over his shoulder as he left the car. He thought this might be a long night, and wanted to be sure he had his toiletries and a quick change of clothes. His journal was also tucked inside an interior pocket. He leaned forward and took off the pack, setting it down next to the sofa.

Christine never even noticed. She was busy in the kitchen, humming to her movements as she prepared the food. Her face was lit from within and she seemed to have become a younger version of herself.

Brian watched her warily. He was not certain of her mood and had learned the hard way to not reveal himself or his feelings. Christine could be unstable at times, and her emotions would completely rule her behavior to the point that she could not hear reason.

Watching her preparations, he could not help himself by asking, "Are we going to watch a movie?"

She laughed gaily and smiled warmly. "No, silly. I just wanted us to be comfortable while we talk. I have so much to tell you!" As she handed him one of the wine glasses, she said with a laugh, "But after you hear my story, you might think you were watching a movie!"

Brian shook his head at her gay mood and took a sip of wine. He had no clue what was coming, but he might as well enjoy her company and being back home as long as he could.

After she had eaten several pieces of cheese and crackers and took a sip of her wine, she explained, "I missed dinner so I was starving." She paused for a beat, and then said in wonder, "And I took TWO naps today!"

Brian knew better than to question her about her eating habits, especially since he had moved out of the house. But the information about it being a two napper day was too much to resist.

"What in the world made you take two naps? You never take naps!" he exclaimed.

"I know – it's crazy," she said laughing. "But after you hear what happened today, you will see why I had to shut down for a few minutes."

He waited expectantly for her to begin. She took a deep breath and said sincerely, looking deeply into his eyes, "I am so sorry about over-reacting this afternoon." She shook her head and said, "I was a coward and should have trusted my instincts. Instead, I acted out of fear and pushed you away again." She looked up at the ceiling for inspiration and took another cleansing breath. "Just like I have done since I ended our pregnancy."

The statement shimmered in the air, unadulterated and unadorned.

She held her breath and waited for him to accept or reject her apology. He gazed at her thoughtfully, weighing the sincerity of her words against her past actions. The fact that she said "our pregnancy" gave him hope that she had really turned a corner and forgiven herself.

"Go on," he said noncommittally.

"I've realized many things about myself today," she continued. "But the most important thing I realized is that I acted totally out of fear." She stopped and gathered herself before she admitted, "And I made a unilateral decision that should have been made by the both of us."

He nodded in agreement but still did not speak. He wanted to see how far she would take this discussion.

"I am deeply sorrow for taking over like that – but I knew you would stop me if I told you I was going to see that other doctor." She started crying softly and then whispered bravely, "I just could not handle being the mother of a child with no arms or legs."

Brian looked at her with compassion, knowing that she had finally experienced her dark night of the soul and had looked into the face of her deepest fear. He closed his eyes and silently willed them to move on to another level in their relationship.

He offered his hands to her, squeezing them gently and reassuringly. He tenderly kissed her forehead and let her cry without saying a word. Healing can come in many forms, and he knew that she was reaching past the pain and moving through it.

When he thought she was through, he quietly got up and went to the bathroom for some tissue, which he brought back to her. He refilled their wine glasses and sat down next to her, feeling more peaceful than he had in years. They sat together in the comfortable silence of a long-term relationship, listening to the small night noises outside. An owl hooted somewhere in the distance, punctuating the night with her lonely call.

Brian shifted in his weight and asked gently, "So what happened today that made you so aware of your past decisions?"

Christine smiled at him and laughed. "That's right – I left out a big part of today, didn't I?"

He nodded and waited for her to continue. He could feel how much lighter she was in her demeanor and he was curious about the events that could cause such a seismic shift in her attitudes, beliefs and behavior.

"I don't know where to start," she began. She thought for a minute and then asked him a question, "Have you noticed anything different about Savanna lately?"

He shook his head. "We had a long talk the other night, but she was still struggling with the entire situation. I haven't spoken to her since then, only short text messages." He paused and added as an afterthought, "We were going to spend tomorrow afternoon together."

She nodded. "Well, it all started last week after you left. It has taken us some time to readjust," she added ruefully. She smiled warmly and said, "We both miss you very much."

Brian nodded and smiled back. "I miss you guys too." They shared a quick hug and then Christine got back to her story.

"Actually, your leaving was the best thing to happen to me in a long time!"

Brian looked hurt for a moment but then decided to accept her statement without judgment. He nodded for her to continue.

"I didn't mean that like it sounded," she said, half apologetically and half teasing. "It's just that it was such a shock that it jolted me." Christine paused reflectively before she said, "And it certainly jolted Savanna – she is not the same person."

Brian was about to ask about the changes in their daughter when something told him to not interrupt. He said instead, "Go on..."

"Well, last Sunday night, we had a long talk. Actually, she demanded to know what we were keeping from her and I told her the story about the baby." Pain and shame flitted over her expressive features as she recalled that night with her daughter.

Brian's raised eyebrows spoke volumes. "You told her the whole story?" he exclaimed in disbelief.

She nodded calmly. "Actually, I decided that it was time that she knew. Plus, I wanted her to understand why you left and that it didn't have anything to do with her."

Brian released a breath that he did not know he was holding. "Thank you," he said softly. He recognized how much courage it took for her to admit her part in the drama of their earlier lives. He appreciated that fact that she gave an honest account and did not blame him, which could have poisoned his relationship with his daughter.

She smiled and said, "It was the right thing to do. Savanna was ready to hear it and deserved to know what happened to make you leave." She paused as she remembered the emotional scene from the night before. "But she was not happy, let me tell you!"

Brian nodded. "Did she totally erupt or did she go into stealth mode?"

Christine answered with love in her voice, "On a scale of one to ten, she blew a fifteen."

He chuckled knowingly, thinking how passionate Savanna could be about seeing a hurt dog by the side of the road. He could only imagine the ugly scene when her mother finally revealed the family's darkest secret.

"So how long did it take for her to calm down?" he asked in concern.

Christine thought about the events that took place since Brian had left. "Oh, about a week," she answered. "I'm not sure what the change was, but today she suddenly opened up to me and then took me to the park."

Brian's surprise showed in his eyes. "The park?" he asked. "What's so special about the park?" There was no need to define which park they referred to – it was the same one that they used to take Savanna to when she was younger, to look at the ducks.

Christine smiles at his inquiry. "I had the same reaction...but this is where the story gets good," she said with a wink. "Are you ready for this?" She asked playfully.

He sat up straighter and said hesitantly, "I guess so..." He had no idea what she was going to say.

She thought for a moment, and then said, more to herself than to him, "I'm just going to tell it like it happened. He can believe me or not." She stole a glance at him to gauge his reaction, but his face remained cloaked behind a mask that she could not read.

She plunged into what happened that day, starting with their bicycle ride to the park that morning, their fight over Avery and her falling asleep under the tree. Then she got to the part about her dream, and her rendition faltered.

Brian was not sure where all of this was going, but he did know that he had his wife back. Whatever happened in the park, he was ready to accept and thank for the amazing transformation in his spouse. He could accept anything.

Except Christine meeting her spiritual self.

When she came to that part of the narration, Brian immediately stood up and said, "I don't believe it!" She looked at him in surprise and then embarrassment, knowing that she could have described her experience in more believable terms. Instead, something inside of her broke open.

"Brian Hartt," she began indignantly. "How can you stand there and say I did not meet my spiritual self, when you can see the difference it made with your own eyes!" She glared at him in frustration and silently willed him to listen.

He was stunned by her conviction. He shook his head at her tirade and decided for the sake of peace in the family, to not argue with her. "But how in the world did that happen?" he wondered silently to himself.

"I'm sorry honey," he began in the same soothing voice he would use to someone who is about to jump off a cliff. "It's just that it is a little hard to believe," he added lamely.

"Have you ever known me to make up something that wasn't true?" She asked incredulously. But as soon as the words were out of her mouth, she knew that she had made a huge mistake. She braced herself, waiting for the direct attack that was sure to follow, when Brian did something extraordinary.

He laughed!

After he regained control of himself, he turned to her and said, humor underlying every syllable, "Do you REALLY want me to answer that?"

She shook her head sheepishly and said, "Oops." She stole a peek at him to make sure that he was laughing with her, instead of at her, and continued. "Guess I really stuck my foot in my big fat mouth that time!" They shared the joke and then Brian asked her to continue.

"Let's skip past the part about me meeting the woman," she offered. When he nodded his agreement, she continued. "Savanna came back to the park and found me, and then we came back here and had a great talk." Christine smiled and said, "And that is when you happened to stop by while I was taking a nap."

Brian grinned and said, "I couldn't believe it when Savanna said you were lying down upstairs. I had to go see for myself!"

Christine nodded. "I didn't know you were in the bedroom until I came out of bathroom. You startled me!"

He smiled apologetically. "Sorry about that," he said. When I saw how peaceful you were sleeping, I decided to take advantage of the opportunity for my own nap."

She grinned and said the tag line to an old family joke, "The Napster strikes again!"

They sat in silence for a few seconds, and then she continued. "After you left, I was so depressed. I couldn't believe that I let myself go back to fear, instead of staying with the love I felt in my dream." She paused and said regretfully, "I did try to stop you from leaving, but you were already in your car by the time I got to the front door."

Brian squeezed her hand. "I needed to leave and cool down," he explained gently. He shook his head and admitted, "I was not ready to be rejected again after I thought..." The sentence hung in the air, waiting to be completed. Caution tinged with a small bit of hope made him leave it unsaid.

She nodded in understanding of his vulnerability. "After you left, I wasn't sure what I was going to do," she said, more to herself than to him. "Savanna and I talked some more and then she took me to the forest to meet her new friend."

Now it was Brian's turn to be upset. "You mean that since I've been gone, you let my daughter meet strangers in the woods?" his voice rising incredulously at the thought.

Christine almost reacted to the derisive tone but was able to stop herself in time. "Just wait," she said, patting his hand. "It gets even better when you find out who it was!"

Her reassurances did little to calm his protective fatherly instincts. He took several deep breaths and motioned for her to continue.

"We rode our bikes to the woods on the other side of the park. There is a small road..." Christine stopped as soon as she realized that she was giving directions to Avery's cabin. Her mind flashed back to earlier that night when Avery adamantly demanded that no one know about the cabin, even if it meant that her mother would not receive the medical treatment she needed. Christine knew that the location of the cabin was meant to be kept a secret, so she smiled at Brian and said hastily, "And then we stopped and a magical mailbox appeared."

A raised eyebrow greeted her slight alteration to her story. "That was the problem of someone knowing you as well as you knew yourself," she thought ruefully.

"What do you mean, 'a magical mailbox appeared'?" He asked abruptly.

"Maybe I shouldn't describe it as magical, but it is very unusual," she said, excitement tingeing her voice with energy.

Brian could not help himself from reacting. "Are you going to tell me that the mailbox is spiritual too?" he asked derisively. He knew that he sounded harsh and uncaring, but his defenses were automatically triggered anytime she mentioned or inferred that she was in touch with the spiritual side of life.

Christine sat back on the sofa and took a minute to look into his eyes. She could see doubt and fear, mixed with trepidation. Less than 24 hours ago, she would have reacted the exact same way. She realized that he needed time to adjust and that if she told him the whole story about what happened today, he would not hear it.

And she wanted, more than anything in the world, for him to *hear* it. When the judgmental part of his mind was quiet and his heart was open to receive. She said a silent prayer, asking for guidance. It did not take long for her to receive her answer.

She smiled at him lovingly and stood up slowly, stretching her arms above her head. She pulled him up and said, "You know what? It's really late and I need to go to sleep. Tomorrow is Sunday…" Christine glanced at the large clock hanging over the kitchen counter and laughed. "Actually, it's already Sunday. What don't you sleep here on the sofa and we can talk more in the morning?"

Brian nodded in agreement. He gave her a quick hug and she turned to get pillows and bedding from upstairs. After they had his bed set up, she lightly kissed him and said as she was turning out the light, "This will make so much more sense in the morning." He nodded and sat down on the sofa, waiting for her to leave.

As soon as she went upstairs, he turned the lamp back on and pulled his journal from his daypack. He thought over what his wife had shared with him tonight, and wrote it down in his precise handwriting. He allowed the judgmental thoughts to surface and continued writing, not censoring or stopping the flow. After he filled more pages than he could count, he slowly set down his pen and reached over to turn out the light.

He lay down on the soft comforter, settling himself against the pillows, and stared up at the cove ceiling. Shadows played on the flat surface, created by the patio light outside and the wind moving through the trees. He felt emotionally drained listening to Christine, not understanding what caused her dramatic transformation and coming to terms with the arc of events that occurred to the two people he loved the most.

Brian knew he was over-reacting to the "spiritual" side of Christine's story, but he never understood why people would get excited over spiritual ideas. He always thought of those types as "woo-woos" who didn't have a clue about real life. He was comfortable with his Christian ideals and knew just how far he could go in his relationship with God. Anytime he was presented with concepts that fell outside those well-defined boundaries, he felt uncomfortable. And reacted derisively, without any thought to whether it might just be true.

Mystical thinking was so...vague and undefined. You couldn't taste it or touch it. The "woo-woo" folks just wanted you to *believe* that it was true because they said so. They didn't have more than 2,000 years of theology to back them up; they only had their word that it was so. Brian always felt turned off by their assertions and...yes, their "spiritual superiority." He just didn't buy it, no matter how passionately they argued their beliefs.

He enjoyed knowing the rules of life. Treat others like you want them to treat you; don't cheat or hurt another; forgive others so you are forgiven. Those rules (as well as many others) were very doable and easily understood. They were written in the Bible and therefore must be true.

But something nagged at him...something important. What was it?

All was not what it seemed.

He hummed to himself as he let his mind wander. A tingling of recognition swept over him when he realized what bothered him.

His conservative Christian upbringing did not necessarily encourage a direct relationship or conversation with God. Brian believed that Jesus was his gateway to God. But didn't Jesus himself insist that everyone was a child of God? He also said repeatedly that God was *our* Father, who loved us more than we could ever imagine.

Brian continued to allow his thoughts to wander. Suddenly, a flash of inspiration made him take a sharp intake of air. A thought struck him like a blow, and he could only stare at the darkened ceiling in amazement. And wonder why he had never considered it before.

Instead of Brian contemplating how he should see God...now he wondered... *how did God want to be seen?*

Brian lay stunned on the sofa as that realization sunk into his entire being.

God wants to be seen...and loved.

The discord and dissention between various churches, religions and even countries about God was really unnecessary when considered from God's viewpoint. He just wants to be seen...in everything, in every moment to the beat of every heart.

To be seen meant that Brian would have to know God...and to know God meant that he had to have a relationship with him. And the basis of any strong relationship was communication...and love.

"Of course!" Brian thought in amazement. "God wants us to know him and be in a personal relationship with him!" The enormity of this insight was stunning in its simplicity.

Brian recalled the strong sense of *knowing* that he experienced when he finally asked God directly for help. Didn't he receive an answer immediately? It was almost as if God were waiting expectantly for Brian to *ask* for help. Not demand, not plead, just a simple request made from a sincere place in his heart.

All he had to do was ask, and God was there.

There was no doubt in his mind that he had a conversation with God. That single incident changed the trajectory of his life from bitterness to forgiveness. Wasn't that more in line with what Christine was describing – more in the spiritual realm than the religious?

He had experienced his own connection to the Divine. Why was he so dismissive of his wife having a similar experience?

Brian Hartt prided himself on being fair and open-minded. He knew that he had judged Christine too quickly and too dismissively. Because of his knee jerk reaction, he did not appreciate the valuable insights that she had gained from her recent experience.

He only hoped that he was able to keep his mind open when he heard the full story tomorrow. And not react as if it were spiritual mumbo-jumbo...

Brian also knew intuitively that there was much more for his wife to tell him, but he was grateful that she had stopped when she did and called it a night.

A sudden thought came to him, one that he had not fully considered before now. What was it that Christine had asked him when she started telling her story tonight? Something about whether he noticed any differences in Savanna...

Was Savanna part of this spiritual web too?

It was too much to think about. He knew that he had a lot of catching up to do, because obviously both his wife and his daughter had been through a life-changing experience...without him. His male ego was dinged a bit from that realization. He sighed deeply, wondering where they were all going from here.

Just before sleep overcame him, the one question that concerned him the most floated into his awareness.

"What if it is all true?"

16

Dance of the Hartts

Life is a dance, from one stage to the next. ~ Anonymous

Sundays were usually casual in the Hartt household. No alarms, no need to get up too early, except to go to church service at 10:30. The late night took its toll on all of the members of the family, including the cat, Bandelier. Normally, she was crying to be let outside at 6:00 a.m., but even she was still asleep after the bird clock in the kitchen chirped at 9:30.

Savanna stretched long in her bed as she considered the possibilities of her day. She wanted to go to the hospital and make sure that Janet and Avery were O.K. She also wanted to call her dad and share with him all that had happened yesterday.

After getting up, going to the bathroom and brushing her hair, she grabbed her cell to text him. They were supposed to do something special today, and she wanted to know what it was. She was not ready for his reply.

"Come downstairs."

Savanna shook her head in amazement. How could he be downstairs? Wasn't he at his apartment? Maybe he had decided to stop by the house earlier than they had planned. Maybe...she could almost not bear to think about the next hope that sprang up inside her heart.

Maybe, he was here to stay.

She ran down the flight of stairs, almost flying in anticipation. She skidded around the corner into the den, only to come to an abrupt halt as she saw her parents sipping coffee on the deck, casually talking and laughing.

Savanna took a moment to just watch them. They had no idea that she was there, but she could sense that they had somehow come back together. She said a quick 'thank you' to God, grabbed a pack of orange juice, and opened the French doors to join them.

Her dad stood up immediately. "Hi honey," he said casually, as he grabbed her in a big bear hug. "Bet you're surprised to see me!" he said teasingly as she pulled away. Savanna glanced over at her mother, who smiled lovingly at both of them. She looked serene and peaceful, sitting in the same lounge chair where only yesterday she had completely fallen apart.

The contrast was dramatic and would have overwhelmed most people. But Savanna had stepped into her larger awareness and she could now see that, although painful, it was a necessary process for her mother.

Savanna sat down on the end of her mother's chaise lounge chair and looked at them both with love. "I can see that a lot must have happened after I went to bed last night," she noted, a hint of teenager exasperation in her voice for having missed out on the drama.

Her father nodded and said, "Your mother and I have been talking. She was telling me about what happened to you both yesterday." He paused thoughtfully while he added, almost to himself, "I still don't understand."

Christine added, slightly frustrated but without a hint of sarcasm, "He doesn't believe me."

Savanna nodded and said in the deep falsetto voice of a television announcer, "And now we bring you 'Tales of the Spirit' sponsored by Miracle Whip."

Both of her parents looked at her as if she had just sprouted two heads and both were speaking at the same time. Savanna held onto her serious expression, until it nearly killed her, then she broke character and started laughing. Soon, her father's deep chuckle was followed by her mother's lighter, breathier laugh.

After they settled down, Savanna motioned for her dad to sit back down in his chair. She patted his knee and said sweetly, "It happened just the way she said."

Brian felt looser and more relaxed after the comic relief provided by his daughter, and his mind opened just a bit to allow in the possibility of connecting to the spiritual world. But he was a long way from being convinced.

"Actually, your mother never did finish telling me about yesterday," he said as he looked at Christine with a loving glance. "Why don't you pick up where you left off last night?"

She shook her head. "Can't we just enjoy our Sunday morning together? There is plenty of time to fill you in on the details."

Savanna knew that her mother wanted to process all of the new knowledge and information she had learned from Avery and Janet Andersen, before she explained it to Brian. Savanna winked at her mother and stood up, stretching.

"This is loads of fun, but I think I may go inside and write in my journal."

Brian looked up in surprise at his daughter. "So you listened to me, did you?" he asked with a sly grin.

She nodded and said, "It really helped me get through this last week." She hesitated, and then added, "Of course, meeting Avery and Avatar..." As soon as she said their names, she knew from the shocked expression on her father's face and the slightly horrified look on her mother's that she had stepped into new territory. She started to slowly back away before her dad could ask her more questions.

No such luck.

"Don't you slink away from here just yet, young lady," he said sternly. "Who are Avery and Avatar and how come I don't know anything about them?"

Savanna glanced at her mother for help, but she was looking down at her hands, clenched in her lap. Savanna faced her father squarely and said, in a calm and even tone, "They're my new friends. Mom has met them – she can tell you all about them!" Savanna smiled and turned towards the house, sending her mother waves of love and support.

Unfortunately, Christine did not receive even a drop of love. Instead, her heart rate accelerated, causing the carotid artery in her neck to pulse. While she tried to compose herself, Brian waited, tapping his finger on the chair's arm a bit impatiently.

Finally, Christine took a deep breath and turned towards her husband. She knew the next few minutes would be difficult and she prayed for support and guidance. Then she began telling him about the events from yesterday.

"Where did I leave off?" she asked him, silently begging him to be patient.

"You said that after I left yesterday, that you and Savanna had a nice talk out here on the deck, and then you guys rode to the park, had a fight and you fell asleep under the tree." He stopped abruptly, because that is when she claimed to have met her "spiritual self."

She smiled in understanding at his discomfort. "It's O.K. if you don't believe me. I realize now that everyone has to accept the larger truths in their own time and in their own way. I can't force you to believe me and I certainly won't try."

Just hearing those words made Brian relax his tense muscles. He had not realized how much of his resistance was because he did not want to be forced to believe her in order to salvage their relationship. Just knowing that he did not have to accept everything was a huge relief. He nodded for her to continue.

Christine reached over to hold his hand and began telling him about the rest of yesterday's events. At several parts, he tried to take his hand back, but she held onto it like the lifeline that it was to her. By the time she finally got to the part where she sent him the text message, she was exhausted.

She glanced over at him and could see that he was looking far off into the distance, thinking about everything she had described. He finally spoke.

"I will not have you letting Savanna meet strangers in the park," he said in his "lawyer" voice. Whenever he wanted to assert his authority at home, his voice would drop to a deeper level and his tone would drip with authority. Christine and Savanna called it his "Judge" voice.

"And I do not want her to see this 'Avery and Avatar' again." Brian paused to add emphatic emphasis to his next statement. "They sound too alien to be from around here."

Christine looked at him, shocked that he could be so dense. Then she realized that she had left out a very important detail about who Avery and Avatar were and how they knew them.

"Oh Brian, stand down," she said, exasperated at his overly protective fatherly tone. "I just realized that I forgot one very important detail that will make you feel better." She paused and said, "But you have to apologize to me first."

Brian shook his head vehemently. "I have never doubted your mothering skills before, but I just can't see how..."

He never finished his sentence, because just then, the doorbell rang.

Christine sat up in the chair and swung her legs over the side. "Who in the world could that be on a Sunday morning?" she said, as she walked into the house and opened the front door. Savanna also came down the stairs from her room, and they both waited expectantly to see who was on their front porch.

The door swung wide to reveal Janet Andersen, Avery and Avatar. Before anyone could say anything, Avatar darted into the house and ran up to Bandelier, who was napping peacefully in the chair. Bandelier jumped up, back arched and ears back, snarling as her fur blew up to twice its normal size. Before any of the humans could stop her, she swatted Avatar on the nose, which caused him to slink down, and slide back to Avery, whimpering.

Christine was the first to react. She shooed Bandelier outside and then turned to see if Avatar was injured. There were droplets of blood on his face, but he seemed to weather the experience with dignity.

Avery checked her dog carefully, and then said to the group, "He's obviously never met a cat before." The look on her face said that he probably wouldn't again. Christine invited them into the house, and quickly checked Janet's head to make sure her wound had not opened up again. She smiled at their guests and asked them to wait a minute while she went to get her husband, who was still sitting outside on the deck.

Brian was seething from their earlier conversation. He had no idea who these people were or why they were so important to Christine and Savanna. It hurt his feelings that they could have gotten so comfortable in their new life without him that unknown friends would stop by unannounced. Of course, the fact that he was the one to move out was beside the point.

If it was possible for a grown man to pout, it would have been Brian Hartt.

He shot a glaring look at Christine, and said abruptly, "I'll just go out the back way." He turned to go, when she stopped him.

"Please stay just a minute. I promise you that all of this will make so much more sense if you will just stay and meet these people."

He glanced back inside and thought he recognized the older woman, who was watching Savanna play on the floor with the dog. He took a step closer and got a better look.

"What is Janet Andersen doing in our house?" he asked, shocked and somewhat offended. "Have you been going back to her for counseling without me?" His tone was rather strident, as one surprise after another continued to be thrown at him.

Christine laughed lightly. "No, I haven't been going to her for counseling! Remember, we tried that years ago and it didn't work." She smiled at his discomfort and again invited him to come inside so he could hear the rest of the story.

Brian had calmed down somewhat, so he reluctantly followed his wife inside, feeling like a stranger in his own home. He greeted Janet kindly but kept his distance. When he was introduced to Avery, he took a moment to look more closely at her.

"Are you and Janet related?" he asked hesitantly.

The innocent question drew an immediate response from the crowd. Everyone started giggling, then laughing. He felt like an idiot for not knowing the punch line. Just as he was about to turn and leave, Christine took pity on him.

"Brian, this is Avery and her dog, Avatar – from the park!"

Both Christine and Savanna waited expectantly while he digested this information. Before he could ask any more questions, the two Hartt women said in unison, "Avery is Janet's daughter!"

Brian's brown eyes grew wide in surprise, and then closed in embarrassment. He turned to Christine and said, "I am so sorry, honey." She squeezed his hand reassuringly and whispered for his ears only, "We'll talk later."

Next he turned to his daughter and gave the same apology. She was more effusive in her acceptance and impulsively reached up and hugged him fiercely. "I don't hang out with strangers, Daddy," she whispered in his ear as he squeezed her tight.

He turned toward Janet and her daughter to make his apologies. Janet stopped him and said, "We understand how all of this can be intimidating. It is quite alright to not jump into the pool, so to speak, right away." She smiled warmly and added, "All in good time." Brian visibly relaxed his body, and felt his mind and his attitude adjust as well.

Brian could not help but notice the large bandage on Janet's forehead and the protective manner that Avery showed to her mother.

"What happened?"

Janet shook her head and said, "I had a bit of a spell last night, fell and hit my head. After 10 stitches and a lot of testing, they released me from the hospital."

Avery added, "We grabbed a cab to get here. Our car is in the drive and we need to give Christine a ride so she can get her car."

Christine nodded and turned to her husband. "Avery doesn't drive and Janet was in no condition to. So I drove her to the hospital in her car. Mine is still at..."

Avery interrupted and said quickly, "It's in a safe place."

Brian noted the undertones of the conversation but decided that now was not the best time to explore it. He smiled at their guests and told Janet that he hoped she would recover fully.

Christine, ever the gracious hostess, guided everyone outside onto the deck. As she went back inside for refreshments, Savanna pulled Avery away and took her upstairs. "I wanted to show you my room," she confessed to her mentor, friend and ally.

As the adults settled down in the comfortable chairs and the peaceful backyard, Christine brought out hot tea, scones and fruit, artfully arranged on a beautiful ceramic tray. It was glazed in unusual colors, ranging from the deepest grays to subtle blue, and every shade in between. The shape was long and elliptical, graceful in design and almost fluid.

As she set it down, Janet Andersen smiled at Christine. "I see that you still take time to make ceramics."

Christine laughed as she sat down on the other side of her husband. "That's right, I had forgotten. You were the one to suggest that I find a creative outlet after the ba..." She couldn't get the word out, not with her husband sitting next to her and her former marriage counselor watching her.

Janet immediately understood Christine's discomfort, and easily slipped into her former counselor mode, almost as if she had never left it. "When did you make this piece?" she asked, deflecting the attention away from the past that bound them together.

Christine was about to answer, when Brian jumped in first. "It was right after Savanna was born," he said proudly. "I always said that she could have made a go as an artist..."

Christine blushed and grabbed his hand in gratitude. "Thank you," she said, love beaming from her eyes. He gave her a look that said, "We'll talk later," and turned his attention back to Janet.

Janet watched the exchange and relaxed. The last time she had seen these two people in a counseling session, their conflicts were deep-rooted and seemingly insurmountable. When she became Principal of Newridge High School, she had only seen Christine around school. Brian had kept away from that part of his daughter's life.

"So Avery is your daughter," Brian began, leading the conversation back to more recent events.

Janet nodded. "She was living with her father in California when I first saw you in counseling. She came back here only a few months ago."

Understanding dawned. "So that's why I never knew that you had a daughter!"

"When she first left, I was devastated," Janet continued. "It was about that time that I saw the two of you." Pain flittered across her features but was replaced with her usual expression of compassionate understanding. "We have been getting to know each other again," she added softly.

Christine's hand flew to her mouth. "That must have been so hard for you, listening to us and still feeling the loss of Avery."

Janet's slight nod and small smile acknowledged the truth of that statement. "It was hard. But out of that time came my greatest growth." She paused and added, "There were so many things I learned, that I never would have been able to accept if Avery were living with me."

Brian shook his head in disbelief. "But your daughter left you. How could any good come from that loss?"

"It's so hard for us to see the big picture," Janet explained. "Avery left on her own. She was fifteen years old, and already knew that she had a unique connection to God." Janet paused and then continued, "My husband and I had already divorced and he moved to San Diego for his job. There was a very unusual school in San Diego that Avery wanted to attend. I could see that she really wanted to explore that side of her experience, so I let her go."

"Don't you regret that?" Brian asked.

Janet leaned forward so she could look him directly in the eyes. "Not for a minute," she said emphatically. "I needed the space to grow and so did she." Janet glanced at Christine and said, "And now, Avery has returned and we are closer than ever."

Brian just could not accept letting a child go her own way at such a young age. He thought about the sacrifice Janet made, to be a long-distance parent so her daughter could go to school and be with her dad. "You must love her very much," he concluded softly.

Janet nodded and said with a smile, "When we make decisions out of love, everyone involved expands and grows. When we allow fear to define and decide for us, we constrict and limit ourselves."

The weight of her words settled on Brian and Christine. Neither one said anything as they each considered her statement and found it to be true in their own experience.

Christine was the first to recover. "I shut both you and God out of the situation," she said softly, looking at Brian for some indication that he was willing to talk about her past decision that drove them apart. She continued, more to herself than to the others, "And look at what a mess it made."

Janet held up her hand to emphasize her point. "Remember, Christine, castigation and guilt keep you locked into your story. You have moved beyond that, haven't you?"

Christine nodded gratefully, tears beginning to pool in her eyes, making them shimmer a deeper blue than normal. "I still do that!" she cried in exasperation. "When will I stop doing that?"

"It takes time to unlearn everything you thought you knew," Janet reminded her. "Remember who you are and go from there. You'll quickly learn to recognize when your ego is tricking you into playing small."

Brian watched this entire exchange with interest. He could tell that he had a lot of catching up to do, but he enjoyed seeing his wife relax and remain open to advice. For the last 16 years, Christine had held onto herself with a rigidity that was hard to accept. Now, she acted more like the carefree young woman he had fallen in love with at college.

He cleared his throat to gain their attention. "What do you mean about Christine's 'story'?"

Janet nodded at the change in direction and said, "Events are neutral. The cup falls, water spills, an accident happens. It is only when we place our judgment on the event that it takes on meaning for us. As we create our 'story' about what happened that makes sense to us, we believe that it is true." She paused for a heartbeat, and then continued, "And it *is* true...for us."

Brian followed the logic to its ultimate conclusion. "So what one person believes happened is based on the story they created about events that are really neutral. But their story will not necessarily be true for anyone else." He paused to let the truth of the words sink in.

Janet smiled at his foray into the discussion. "There is only one great truth that never changes, never deviates and applies to every single person on the planet." She winked and asked, "Want to know what it is?"

Both Christine and Brian nodded, eyes slightly wider than usual, breath held expectantly. Christine grabbed Brian's hand and waited. She already knew what the one great truth was, but she prayed with all of her heart that Brian accepted it as she had.

"The one great truth is that God loves you more than you could ever imagine," Janet said with utter conviction. "And the best part is that you are loved no matter what you did in your past."

Silence surrounded them, but turmoil roiled inside of Brian's mind as he tried to accept the words he just heard. His resistance to the idea of total and unconditional love was a knee-jerk reaction to years of preachers saying the same thing from the pulpit. It always bothered him that the "unconditional love" concept seemed diametrically opposed to the laws and rules that ran his professional life. He was a small town lawyer. It was hard to believe in unconditional love when people did horrible things to others without regard for the consequences.

He said the first thing that came to his mind. "But doesn't that mean that everyone can do whatever they want, because God will still love them?"

Janet nodded. "That's true," she said. "But you are forgetting one important piece of the equation." She waited for Brian to calm down. "Think of it this way. Every one of us has a drop of God in us that is part of our cells...our DNA. No scientist will be able to dissect and identify it, but in your heart of hearts, you know that it's true, don't you?" She looked expectantly at Brian and waited for his response.

"I guess..." he said reluctantly.

She continued her explanation. "For the purposes of this discussion, let's call that bit of God your 'spiritual self.'"

Brian's reaction was instantaneous. "I'm sorry, Janet," he said. "But that is where I always feel myself go off track."

Janet understood completely. "We are talking about concepts that may bring up resistance." She thought for a moment and continued, "In order to continue our discussion, you might be more comfortable with the word 'soul.'"

Brian nodded in agreement. "I guess that comes from years of listening to the Minister at Church talking about 'saving my soul from damnation,'" he said ruefully.

"These are just terms or symbols of something much bigger than we can imagine," Janet said, understanding the confusion that Brian must be feeling but wanting to continue her explanation. "Let's not get hung up on the words. Are you willing to listen to the message?" she asked gently.

When he reluctantly nodded, she continued, "Good. So we agree on the term 'soul.'" Janet paused as a sudden thought struck her. "I just remembered something!" she said in an excited voice.

Christine had been listening intently and could not wait to hear the next words. "What is it?" she prodded.

Janet took a deep breath and centered herself. "I just thought of this before we drove over here this morning." She paused for dramatic effect then said, "An easy way to think of 'soul' is to remember what it stands for. It's the key to everything!"

Brian's full attention was directed at this woman who had seen both he and his wife at their absolute worst. He could not imagine what she would say that would explain all of the concepts he had heard this morning, but he was willing to listen.

Janet continued with an air of presenting a great gift to her listeners. She smiled at both of them and said softly, "The word 'soul' stands for Source of Unlimited Love."

Silence rained down on the three people as the weight of the words filtered through their consciousness. They each instinctively recognized the spiritual truth of the words, but Brian could not let go of his analytical mind. He admitted both to himself and to the others, hesitation defining his voice, "I still don't get it."

Janet smiled in understanding. "Don't let your rational mind try to figure this out. You have to step away from that type of thinking and just let the truth be accepted."

Christine returned from her reverie and took her husband's hand. "You will get it, I promise," she said as she lovingly squeezed to emphasize her point. "Look, if I can understand all of this – remember, I am the most stubborn person on earth – then you can too!"

Brian's look of shock dissolved quickly at the joke his wife just made at her own expense. He shook his head in wonderment at the dramatic change in her and knew that he wanted to join her on this new level of awareness. Laughter filled the air and they hugged.

After a few moments, Janet stood up to leave them alone. Brian stopped her by saying, "Please don't leave. I really want to hear more about why the 'soul' is the key to everything."

Janet sat back down and continued. "Would you agree that everyone has a 'soul'? Especially the way that I just defined it – 'Source of Unlimited Love.'"

Both Brian and Christine nodded. Janet smiled and then asked in her teacher voice, wanting her students to supply the answer, "And if the word 'soul' means 'Source of Unconditional Love,' what does that mean for every person on the planet?"

Christine was the first to venture an answer. "It means that everyone has their own personal connection to God!"

Janet smiled in approval and continued. "So if everyone has their own connection, why aren't they using it?"

Brian's eyes glimmered as he carried that question to its logical conclusion. "Because they chose not to."

Both Christine and Janet looked at him in amazement. Maybe he was not so dense after all. Brian shrugged his shoulders and held up both hands as if to say, "Give a guy a break." They all laughed and the mood lightened considerably.

Janet was the first one to recover. "So if everyone has a 'soul' and it is the Source of Unconditional Love, where do you suppose that love comes from?"

Both Christine and Brian glanced at each other, and said simultaneously, "From God!"

Janet clapped her hands at her students in approval and continued, "Think of it this way. If your 'soul' comes from God, doesn't it make sense that it is still connected to God?"

She waited for them to acknowledge the truth of her words. She paused for emphasis, and then added, "And the greatest part is that your 'soul' can guide you if you let it."

Christine was still holding onto Brian's hand. She squeezed it and said, "And that is exactly what I learned yesterday."

Brian could still not totally grasp what they were saying, but the joyful look at his wife's face was enough to stop him from being critical or analytical. He took a deep breath to release the tension in his shoulders and said ruefully, "Guess I still have a lot to learn."

Janet nodded her approval at the conscious choice he made to not resist this new information. "Remember, we all learn these truths in our own way and in our own time. How you discover the truth will be totally different than Christine, but that's O.K." She paused before concluding, "That is the whole point of your experience here on earth."

Christine raised an eyebrow at that last statement and asked in slightly frustrated tone, "*What* is the 'whole point of your experience'?"

"To decide who you are...in relation to that."

Brian shook his head. "I don't get it," he said apologetically. He laughed at himself, and muttered under his breath, "I think I have said those four words more in the last hour than I have in my entire life!"

Janet smiled and continued, "Remember when I told you that all events are neutral, until we give them meaning?" They both nodded. "Well, when you give an event meaning, you are making a choice. You are deciding what that event means to you. And you only have one of two choices - either love or fear. You can either make the choice unconsciously or consciously." She paused to let the meaning of her words sink in.

Brian picked up the thread of her statements. "So if our only choice is either love or fear, how does that affect what we experience?"

Janet looked at him with affection. At least he was trying to understand what to him, must be incomprehensible. A lawyer is trained to be at all times, logical and analytical. Acceptance of the spiritual truths she was teaching could never happen with logic and reason. Acceptance had to come from that non-linear, formless essence of being that spoke a completely different language than logic and reason.

She knew that she was trying to explain the unexplainable. But she passionately felt that it was crucial to share this information with others, that she had to at least to communicate as clearly as possible.

Janet sent a silent prayer for the best words to describe it to Brian. After a moment, she said, "Remember that love always expands and fear contracts. When you choose from love, you expand yourself and those around you. When you chose from fear..."

Christine softly finished her sentence. "Everything and everyone involved contracts...or dies." Tears of regret instantly flooded her eyes and she buried her face in her hands.

Brian leaned over and pulled her to him, letting her cry on his shoulder. He glanced over Christine's head at Janet, and saw only love and acceptance. He hugged his wife and helped her clean up her face when the crying jag was finished.

Janet smiled at both of them and said, "Your healing has already begun. Now that you know the effect of choosing between love and fear, you can be more conscious in your decisions."

Brian and Christine both nodded in unison. Gratitude and joy mixed together, along with relief to have finally come to a resting place, together. They sat, hand in hand, peaceful and in love.

Brian broke the spell by asking the pragmatic question that had been bothering him since this conversation started.

"What do we do now?"

Janet smiled and repeated her earlier statement, emphasizing each word slowly and carefully.

"In every moment, you choose Who...You...Are...in...Relation...to...That..."

The statement hung in the air, shimmering with truth. Both Christine and Brian turned inward and discovered that it clarified all of their differences, conflicts and continuing love for each other, despite tragedy, selfishness and pain. They each made different choices about who they were in relation to the baby, which set them off in diametrically opposed directions. No wonder they could never come to terms with those tragic events – each one saw their own position as totally justified and neither could step out of their own story to grasp the other's point of view.

And now, they had another decision to make.

The importance of the moment was not lost on either of them. Christine was the first to move toward her future. She turned to face Brian, took both of his larger hands in her smaller ones, and said gently, "I am so sorry for what I did. I acted out of fear and made a decision on my own, when I should have included both you and God." She paused for strength. "I felt so bad afterwards that I never could let you back into my heart." A deep breath and then she finished, "I love you more than you know. I want to be your wife and live the rest of my days next to your side." She smiled through her tears. "Please forgive me."

Brian's eyes had grown wet and he found that his throat was constricted. No words would come out, so he did the next best thing. He pulled his wife into a fierce hug and murmured into her hair, "I love you."

Janet glanced up at the heavens and said a silent prayer of thanks. She stood up quietly and moved into the house to give them time to talk. A quick glance at her watch told her they had been outside for almost an hour, and she wondered what Avery, Avatar and Savanna had been doing during that time. She decided to go upstairs and check on them.

Her head still hurt from hitting it on the table the night before, and she decided to stop in the small bathroom to check on the bandage. Her face in the mirror showed the stress from being at the hospital overnight, but as she looked deeper into her eyes, she saw it.

Divine light.

Janet smiled and said "Thank you!" winking at her reflection.

17

Story Alchemy

You cannot move forward toward your next big thing
While you are still telling your old story. ~ Kathryn
Eriksen

Just as Janet opened the bathroom door and stepped out, Savanna and Avery walked past. Avatar went in search of the cat, as Janet asked the girls in a hushed voice, "Everything O.K.?"

Avery nodded and smiled at her young student. "Savanna finally figured out what the mailbox initials mean," she said teasingly.

Savanna nodded happily. "I never would have guessed it, but then we started dancing again upstairs..."

Janet smiled and motioned for them to keep their voices down.

Savanna returned the smile and added in a hushed voice, "Why are we whispering?"

"Because your parents are talking outside and I don't want to disturb them," Janet replied.

Just then, Brian came from around the corner to the kitchen. He smiled at the girls and asked Avery, "I couldn't help overhearing your comment about the mailbox. What mailbox are you talking about? And why are the initials so mysterious? Aren't they your initials?

Avery was rather taken aback at the directness of the question but she quickly recovered. She had reached a decision about the location of her cabin and she knew that letting the Hartt family into her life was more important than maintaining secrecy.

Avery smiled at Brian and explained. "The mailbox is at the end of my driveway. I will have to show it to you sometime." She paused as she considered her next words. Avery turned and looked directly at Brian as she said quietly, "And no, they are not my initials."

She turned around and continued walking, effectively ending the conversation. Savanna's shocked gasp was quickly muffled as they continued toward the deck. Her father heard it and looked at her, one eyebrow raised to say, "You and I will talk later." Savanna ducked her head and quickly moved in front of her father to avoid any more inquiries about a delicate subject.

As they approached the chairs, Brian turned back to Avery and said with a hint of hurt for being on the outside while everyone else in the group was not. "I would love to see your home. It has obviously been a place that has become important to my wife and daughter." He smiled to soften his words. "What did you study again in California?"

Avery smiled at his tenacity and knew that she made the right decision about no longer hiding her sanctuary. Brian Hartt would never take "no" for an answer and he would have eventually figured out its location. She felt something inside of her shift and expand and knew that she had made the best decision for all concerned.

"I went to California to study at a very special school," she explained as they settled themselves in the deck chairs. Janet and Christine went back into the house to replenish the drinks and food. Savanna could see that her dad wanted to visit with Avery alone, so she followed the others inside.

Brian turned back to Avery to finish their conversation. "What is the name of your school?"

"The Avalon School of Divinity."

"Is that a school to learn how to become a preacher?"

She laughed and shook her head. "Not quite."

Just then, Avatar stood up and stretched. He wandered back into the house in search of food (and maybe to see if the cat was more hospitable). The break provided Brian an opportunity to consider his next question.

"Then what did you study?"

Avery smiled and acknowledged his curiosity. "Before I can teach others about God, I have to know who I am in relation to God."

"So you studied how to be in a relationship with God?"

"That is a simplistic description, but yes."

Brian decided not to push the point, since he had only met Avery a short while ago. When they knew each other better, they could have a much deeper discussion. He motioned for her to continue her explanation.

Avery was not quite ready to give up so easily. She gazed at the dance of the wind moving through the shimmering aspen leaves, creating beautiful movement. She motioned to the trees and said, "That is how God wants to interact with you."

Brian's puzzled look drew a laugh from Avery. "I just don't get it," he muttered to himself in despair.

"It's O.K to be confused, Brian. You are unlearning all of the rules that have governed your life up to this point."

He turned to her and nodded. "Your mother told me the exact same thing about 30 minutes ago." He took a deep breath and willed himself to relax.

But Avery was not quite finished. She turned back to the sight of the aspen limbs dancing in the sun and said quietly, "Your relationship with God is like a dance – always moving, always creating. Just like the wind moving through those trees."

Brian couldn't help himself. "But I thought that God was constant and encompasses everything."

"He is, but within that constancy are God's relationships. When you were created with the ability to choose – free will – your relationship with God became dynamic."

Brian's legal training kicked into gear. "What do you mean by dynamic?"

"The word dynamic means constant change or motion. So a dynamic relationship with God means that it is always changing or evolving."

Brian shook his head. "I just don't get this spiritual stuff," he muttered to himself. He couldn't help asking the next logical question.

"Why would God want to have an ever-changing relationship with me?"

Avery nodded at his persistence and decision to not give up on this line of inquiry.

"It's simple. Each one of us reflects God back."

The effect of those words was certainly not simple. Instead, their impact propelled Brian out of his chair and his agitation was obvious. He began pacing back and forth as his mind worked out what Avery just said.

"If we 'reflect God' doesn't that mean that we are also God?"

Avery clapped her hands together in approval. "Well done! And you said you didn't get this 'spiritual stuff.'" Her teasing made Brian smile but his agitated pacing did not stop.

"I can't wrap my head around what you are saying," he admitted.

"That is exactly why I went to school – to learn more about it so I could teach it to others."

Brian nodded and finally sat back down, pausing to take a sip of water. His mind was still working on the puzzle and he finally asked another question.

"How do I reflect God?"

Avery looked deeply into his eyes to gage his sincerity. What she saw made her smile and she continued.

"Is it possible for you to see yourself without a mirror or other reflection?"

He thought for a moment and shook his head.

"It is the same way with God."

Brian completed the logical steps. "So God created us so we would reflect God back to God?"

Avery smiled and nodded. She added playfully, "I think of myself as the F.A.C.E. of God." She waited patiently for him to pick up on her message.

"Face?"

She smiled indulgently, loving the feeling of sharing a new concept with a person who had never heard of it before.

"F.A.C.E."

"I have to ask the question – what do the initials stand for?"

She grinned at the game they were playing. "It's simple, really. Don't make too much of it too soon."

He was not going to be put off. "Does F.A.C.E. have anything to do with the mailbox initials?"

Avery's laughter was contagious. Brian picked up on her joyous energy and started laughing with her, even though he had no idea why. He did feel much lighter and freer from their conversation and he let go of his need to understand everything from a logical viewpoint.

After their laughter died down, he looked at Avery and teasingly said, "Well, just tell me what *one* of those sets of initials mean."

She smiled indulgently and responded gently, "F.A.C.E. It stands for Feel A Connection Eternal."

Brian gazed off at the aspen grove that stood majestically at the end of their backyard. He thought about everything that Janet had shared earlier – about the "soul" being the source of unlimited love; about how neutral facts are interpreted, judged and then they become our filter; about how to choose either love or fear in every instance.

And now, he was supposed to believe that he was here to reflect God. That he was the face of God.

One thought did make him pause. He remembered his realization late last night that God wants to be seen, and loved. How did that fit in with being a F.A.C.E.? Brian could feel his mind reeling from the implications of these new concepts.

It was too much, too soon.

He couldn't discount the radical changes in his wife or daughter, but this information was so 'out there' that the basis of his entire life philosophy felt threatened. Even though his defenses were on high alert, he acknowledged the small spark of recognition he felt as Avery described these concepts.

Brian was intrigued with the idea that there could be another set of rules to live by than the ones he knew. He was ever the student and was always curious about new concepts. He was not quite ready to accept these new laws, but after the transformation he had experienced earlier, he would not reject them either.

He came out of his reverie and turned to Avery. "Sometimes I am a slow student, but I want to hear more. Can you give some time to think about what you have told me?"

She smiled at his willingness to keep an open mind. "These concepts are different from what you have been taught," she acknowledged. "They can take a while to understand."

Brian smiled gratefully at being let off the hook. "I do appreciate you helping my wife and daughter. Thank you."

Avery nodded. "They were both ready to learn a different way to see their life."

"And I am not?"

Avery refused to react to his defensive tone. "We are all on different paths. Didn't you acknowledge that when you chose to forgive your wife?"

A look of shock then shame crossed Brian's features. He took a deep breath to steady himself and nodded.

Just then, the others came back outside, preventing any more discussion. Brian quickly got control of his emotions and smiled at his wife as she set down a tray of food. She could see that he was upset, and bent down to kiss him tenderly. She whispered in his ear, "Give it some time."

He nodded and gave her a quick hug, joy flooding his heart to replace the shame he felt earlier. He closed his eyes for a moment and said a quick prayer of thanks.

Avatar moved in between their chairs and his happy grin was directed straight at Brian. He laughed at the invitation and scratched the dog behind his ears, causing his tail to sweep in full motion.

Christine rescued the glasses of ice tea that were placed at the wrong end of the dog, just before his tail was about to knock them over. Everyone laughed and settled into the chairs. Food and drinks were quickly distributed and small talk took the place of more serious discussion.

After a few minutes, Savanna suddenly remembered about the 'Miracle Token' that her mother had given her last night. She pulled the note from her pocket and gave it to Avery. "Have you ever seen one of these before?"

Avery took the paper and gasped in recognition. She seemed to connect to the energy that radiated from the words and she nodded happily. "Where did you get this?" she asked Savanna in wonderment, slightly dazed.

Savanna pointed at her mom, who answered, "It was in my grocery bag yesterday."

Brian reached out for the note and read the words out loud.

You are holding a miracle of a moment in time. Use it wisely.

He glanced up at Avery, questions written all over his face. "Avery, what do you have to do with this?"

She smiled, glowing and said, "Keep reading. Then I will explain."

Brian looked at the note again and read slowly, "*Please add #MiracleToken to your Tweet to let me know you received this message.*" He squinted to read the small print at the bottom and continued, "It's called a 'Miracle Token' and it says that it is 'Universal Currency.' There seems to be a website – www.MiracleIncome.com." Everyone turned to Avery expectantly.

She stood up and twirled around the deck in utter abandon. Avatar barked and began to spin with her. Their dance of celebration slowed as Avery began to get dizzy and wobble a bit. Janet gently guided her back to a chair and they all waited for her to explain why she was so happy.

Finally, after several moments, she calmed down enough to talk. Avatar watched his mistress closely and when he could see that she was alright, he calmly walked over to the water bowl and took a long drink. It was only after he walked back to the group, turned around three times and plopped down with a sigh that Avery began.

"When I was in California, I had to create a project that would fulfill the mission of my school. The Avalon School of Divinity is very committed to its mission of 'sharing the light of love.'

Brian held up the note and asked, "How does this piece of paper share love?" He thought for a moment and then added, "And how can love be light?"

Janet and Christine laughed softly. Brian started to react defensively when Janet leaned over and patted him on his knee. "All in good time, dear."

He took a deep breath to calm his frustration and motioned for Avery to continue.

"My project also had to meet my goals to be a Teacher and help people connect with my work. I had to figure out a way to reach strangers with my message, without being intrusive." Avery paused and glanced at Savanna, giving her a quick wink of acknowledgment. "The key to my work is to be the teacher for the student who is ready."

Savanna nodded in recognition. Looking back over the last week, she could see how she resisted being open to Avery's teaching. She had to let go of her preconceived ideas about God to learn the truth. It was not until she stopped trying to control her family crisis that she learned to see her family's situation from a different viewpoint.

Christine noticed the interaction between the two younger women. She had an entirely new perspective and knew that it was because of Savanna's decision to learn more from Avery. Christine smiled at them both and said, "Avery, we are so glad that you are back home. Your work is so important and will help so many people who are living in emotional pain." She paused thoughtfully then added, "I know it made a big difference to me."

Brian acknowledged his wife's statement by squeezing her hand and taking a moment to look into her eyes with love. He still had the piece of paper in his hand and he held it up, silently asking Avery to continue her explanation.

Avery smiled at these people who had quickly become dear to her. She continued where she had left off. "My project had to be simple, easy to implement and flow easily into people's hands." She glanced at her mother, who nodded for her to continue. "I came up with the idea of 'Miracle Tokens' to be used as 'spiritual currency.'" Avery paused as the amazing sequence of events struck her again. She said in an awed voice, "And one of those Tokens found their way into your bag."

Brian's analytical mind demanded more answers. "But how do these 'Miracle Tokens' get distributed?"

Avery smiled and said, "I set up a website called 'Miracle Income.' When you go to the site and sign up for my emails and I send you Miracle Tokens. You can share them however you are moved to do so, but I envisioned people printing them and giving them to strangers."

Janet spoke up, "When Avery first told me about this project, I was very skeptical. You know how people are...they want to stay in their cocoon of pain and loneliness, not be bothered by some spiritual quote." She looked around the group and added, "But after I saw the various messages and understood the scope of the project, I changed my mind."

"You mean there are different messages?" Brian asked.

Avery nodded. "The whole idea behind Miracle Tokens is that they act like currency. The more you spend them, the more miracles will come back to you."

"So that explains why you say 'Universal Currency' on each one."

"Exactly," Avery smiled. She waited for him to continue with his questions. It did not take long for him to ask the next logical follow up inquiry.

"You said that the more you spend the Tokens, the more 'miracles' come back to you..." Brian's quizzical look prompted Avery to continue her explanation.

"When you see beyond the physical aspect of people or situations and connect with the underlying spiritual energy, you begin to see them in an entirely new way. That change in perspective is what I call a miracle." Avery paused before continuing. "It's all explained in the paper I had to write for school."

Brian was still skeptical. "But what if someone shares a Token but doesn't really believe it will make a difference?"

Avery's eyes lit up at this perfect teaching moment. She leaned forward in her chair to be closer to Brian, who instinctively moved back at the sudden intrusion into his personal space. Avery smiled at his reaction and said gently, "Brian, it's O.K."

All eyes were trained on Brian's face to gage his reaction. He shook his head and laughed at himself, muttering, "Sorry about that. Guess I am still a bit edgy."

The tension eased and Avery picked up the thread of the conversation. "Miracle Tokens are just one of the tangible signs of my project. They are designed to raise the awareness of anyone who happens to come across them, but the Tokens are also a way for people to discover my work."

Although Brian tried to keep the skepticism from his voice, a tinge of it was still apparent when he asked, "And what is your work, exactly?"

"My ultimate goal is to become a Teacher. Someone who is constantly aware of her connection with God and whose thoughts, words and deeds reflect that connection. I am still learning..."

Avery paused as she considered her lesson in fear from the night before. Her mother reached over and squeezed her hand in comfort and support. Avery smiled her thanks and continued.

"Part of my training at the Avalon School was to develop a teachable process to guide people back towards love. Because of my own experiences and understanding of energy and how our thoughts create our reality, I also created a program called "The Story Alchemy Process, 4 Steps to Happiness."

Christine looked intrigued. "Is that what you did to me?"

Avery smiled at her friend and student, before she replied, her voice gentle to soften the message. "Christine, you needed the turbo-charged version of Story Alchemy."

A shocked looked passed over Christine's face as she reacted defensively. It took a moment for her to realize that it was O.K. to need more help. She shook her head and said rather ruefully, "Guess I must be special."

Everyone laughed and Savanna reached over to give her mother a hug of appreciation.

Avery continued her explanation. "My final paper had to describe what Story Alchemy is, how it works and the 4 steps to implement it. I also had to teach practical exercises and techniques so the process becomes part of your daily life."

No one said anything as they digested what Avery had shared. Brian glanced down at the Miracle Token he still had in his hand. His mind was trying to connect the dots and still maintain some relationship with something familiar. He held it up the piece of paper as if it were an exhibit at trial. "But what do Miracle Tokens have to do with the Story Alchemy Process?"

"The Miracle Tokens are one of the practical techniques that people can use to share their connection to God."

Brian shook his head and muttered for the umpteenth time, "I just don't get it."

Avery looked closely at him to gage his sincerity. She could feel that he was struggling with these concepts that were so different from how he ordered his life. Avery did not want to lose him because she moved too quickly. For someone as entrenched as Brian, she would have to let him set the pace.

"Instead of sending you the entire paper, why don't I send you a short summary? Sometimes this new way of thinking can seem a bit overwhelming."

Brian smiled and half-teasingly said, "You're not kidding!"

Janet had been listening to this exchange closely and she thought that she might be able to clarify an important concept for Brian. She glanced at Avery before saying, "It helped me to think of it as 'being seen.' Remember when I told you earlier about what the soul is – Source of Unlimited Love?"

Brian nodded.

"If the 'soul' is the Source of Unlimited Love,' then someone or something has to be the 'source.'

"Makes sense."

"And to tap into that source, you have to be connected, right?"

Brian could sense where Janet was going, but he waited for her to finish her line of thought.

"Before you can establish a connection with anything, you have to be *seen* as a connection point." Janet paused as that concept shimmered in the air. She continued and closed the loop.

"When you see yourself as a point of connection with God, you have accepted that God sees you. Think of it as a two way line – almost like a telephone line - that has to have both ends established before any communication can occur."

Brian paused thoughtfully as he said in wonder, "I just realized last night that God wants to be seen."

This announcement hung in the air for an instant as everyone listening took in its meaning. The group's entire energy raised to a higher level at the thought that God wants to be seen...by them.

Avatar sensed the change in the atmosphere and stood up, stretching his front legs forward while his back legs remained straight. His eyes closed as his head bowed.

Savanna broke the spell by noting, "Look! Avatar is doing the 'downward dog'!"

They all laughed at the timing. Brian was still skeptical about the seeming coincidence and called Avatar over to him. Brian held the dog's big head gently in his hands and looked into his liquid brown eyes, as he whispered, "You knew that all along, didn't you?"

Avatar looked deeply into this man's eyes and allowed the love light to shine through. It only took a few seconds for Brian to feel it, but as soon as the connection was made, Brian pulled back as if he had been shocked. He looked at the dog skeptically and asked more to himself than to anyone else, "How did he just do that?"

The golden retriever calmly sat down and grinned.

Everyone else laughed and Christine leaned over, squeezing her husband's hand in support.

"All of this will start to make sense, honey," she murmured. "Just give yourself time."

Avery smiled at the interaction, and said a silent prayer of thanks for her faithful dog. He could reach people on a different level than she ever could.

After a few seconds, Brian regained control of himself and looked at the group. "Thank you. I obviously have a lot to think about."

Christine knew that her husband was trying to understand but was having a difficult time. She turned back to the group to share her experience. "The first time I felt that I was 'seen' was in my dream. I still can't explain it, but I felt totally accepted and loved." She grew pensive for a moment before finishing her thought. "It was only after I accepted the gift of being seen that I could take a step back and see my past from a new perspective." She smiled at her husband in gratitude for his willingness to come back to her.

Brian was ready to rejoin the discussion. He turned back to Avery, wanting to tie up all of the loose ends. "But how I do get 'seen'?"

The women all shared a quiet laugh as they each thought about how they experienced being seen. Savanna recalled her time in the forest, dancing with the blue orb of light. Christine remembered her dream and the relief she felt when she let go of her story about the baby.

Avery smiled at the sincerity of his question, before saying gently. "That is between you and God." She paused at the puzzled look on his face and added, "God always sees you – that never changes. The question is whether you *see* God."

Brian shook his head in frustration and threw up his hands. "How in the world will I ever actually *see* God?"

Avery began to feel a bit sorry for him, but she could tell that he was willing to learn. She leaned over and said softly, "You have to be willing." She paused dramatically and then added, "A great way to begin is simply to ask."

Before Brian could respond, Avery gently took both of his hands and looked deeply into his eyes. Everyone else held their breath because they knew what was about to happen. They waited for him to react. It did not take long.

His eyes grew wide and he gasped involuntarily, pulling away and breaking the physical and spiritual connection that had been established. He grabbed his chest as short, hard breaths caused his lungs to rise and fall as if he were running a 10K race. Christine calmly reached over and gave him a friendly, supportive hug, which seemed to bring down his anxiety.

"What..." The words refused to come out of his mouth, but he finally took a deep breath, which brought his pulse rate down considerably. Christine smiled at him and gave him a glass of water, which he gulped down gratefully.

Avatar, ever sensitive to energy shifts, woke up, stretched and yawned loudly, breaking the atmosphere. He walked over to Brian and put his large head in Brian's lap, leaning on him. Brian reached down to stroke the dog and looked carefully at Avery.

"Did you learn to do that at school too?" His tone was full of awe and the skepticism that he normally used to shield himself was completely gone.

Avery laughed joyously. "I had to grow into it."

She paused and then decided to push a bit further. "Do you remember what I said before that happened?"

Brian shook his head, because he still couldn't find his footing on firm mental ground. All of the social pretenses were blown away by his glimpse of the Divine and he felt disoriented and confused.

Avery gave him a few minutes to find himself again. She watched him carefully and when she felt he was ready to begin, asked gently, "Do you remember what I said?"

He nodded slowly and answered, "Something about being seen."

Avery nodded and smiled her encouragement. "The Story Alchemy Process takes you through a practice that helps you find your "stories," look at them to see if they are still true for you, and if they no longer serve you, reframe them with a different version."

Brian nodded and asked, without any of his former antagonism, "What does that have to do with being seen?"

"We have already established that the stories we create about the events and people in our life are not absolute truth. They are the basis of what those events or people mean to us. But even though the stories give meaning to our life, they prevent us from being in an authentic relationship with God."

Christine shifted in her chair and said ruefully, "I guess I am the poster child for clutching onto my story and using it as a shield against God." Savanna leaned over and squeezed her mother's arm.

Avery smiled her acceptance of Christine's insight. "Well said, Christine. Stories act as a shield against God. When we believe our story about an event or person, there is no room for God, is there?"

"So when we transform our stories from fear to love, that is when we can be seen?"

The question hung in the air as everyone turned back toward Brian. Amazement then pleasure flicked across Avery's delicate features as she clapped her hands and exclaimed, "Well done!"

Brian ducked his head at the praise and smiled to himself. He could glimpse how different his life would be from this point forward and he actually felt a spark of something that he had not felt in quite some time.

Pure joy and happiness.

"I can see why you call it "alchemy.""

Everyone laughed and Avery responded, "Alchemy has some negative connotations, but when you look at what the early practitioners were trying to accomplish, the same principles apply today."

Brian nodded and took a sip of water as he thought about all of the new concepts he had just heard. It was still too much to absorb in one day, so his mind returned to more practical things. He glanced down at the Miracle Token that had fallen to his lap and picked it up.

"I know I will read about it in your paper, but I still have one question.   You said that when the Tokens are shared, that 'they will come back to you.' What are you talking about?"

Avery smiled slightly at the logical question. She reminded herself that she had to adapt to her audience and share her message in as many different ways as possible so they would understand. She gazed off into the distance and allowed her mind to stop judging or becoming impatient. When she was centered again, she asked gently, "Have you ever spent money?"

Brian laughed and said, "Of course!"

Avery raised her hands, palms up, as if to say, "There you have it."

Janet began to feel sorry for Brian, so she helped him out by adding, "When you spend money, you expect something in return. It's the same thing with Universal Currency...it's just that the return is in a different form." She glanced back at her daughter to see if she had explained it correctly.

Avery nodded in appreciation. "Well said. And that is why I called it 'Miracle Income.'"

Brian waited for a further explanation and realized that he would have to make the connections himself. "So if I circulate Miracle Tokens as a form of Universal Currency, somehow my 'miracle income' will grow?"

Avery clapped her hands in appreciation and said proudly, "Now you've got it!"

Laughter rang out as everyone looked at Brian's expression, which declared in neon lights that he definitely did not 'get it.' He shook his head and said in resignation, "I am so confused."

Christine gave him a quick hug and said brightly, "We have faith in you honey. You'll get it. Just stop being a lawyer and listen with your spiritual self."

He smiled in acknowledgment at his analytical approach to life. "I know I need to lighten up," he admitted, more to himself than to the others. He sat in silence for a few minutes, digesting the information that was just presented. It still made no sense to him, but he did not want to lose his new found connection with his wife and daughter. They seemed to 'get it' so he decided that he would be patient and let them show him the way.

Brian looked down at the Miracle Token that was still in his hand. He decided to venture once more into the mystery behind how this piece of paper found its way into his wife's shopping bag. He turned toward Avery and asked gently, "Why were you so surprised to see that Miracle Token in Christine's grocery bag?"

Avery smiled knowingly at the secret she was about to reveal. "My website has been set up for just a short time. I only shared it with my teachers and some close friends. I was not quite ready for it to go 'public'." She paused thoughtfully and added, "But I guess it isn't my timing that decides...God obviously had other plans!"

Christine finished connecting the dots. She said quietly, "So for someone to put that Miracle Token into my grocery bag means that word of your project spread and someone in Newridge, Colorado printed it!"

Avery nodded and clapped her hands. "Isn't God wonderful?" she cried.

They sat in silence, amazed at the coincidences that must have taken place for that slip of paper to be placed in Christine's bag on the very day that she would be open to its message.

Janet added thoughtfully, more to herself than to the others, "I really love the image that Avery used on the Tokens."

Christine looked at the mosaic image again. "I know that I have seen this somewhere...Avery, where did you take this photo?"

Avery smiled and said, "I was in New York City the summer before my project was due. We took the subway everywhere, and I noticed the beautiful mosaic designs that were part of the walls of different subway stations."

Christine's voice vibrated with excitement. "I knew I had seen that particular mosaic pattern before!" She turned to Brian and said, "Remember, honey, when we went to New York several years ago? I think I pointed out this particular pattern!"

Brian smiled indulgently at his wife. "Honey, you pointed out a lot of things on that trip. If you say that you remember this particular design, then the only thing I can say is, 'of course!'"

Everyone laughed at the happy coincidence.

Janet glanced at her daughter and noticed that she had a distant look in her eyes. "Are you O.K., honey?"

Avery came out of her reverie with a jolt. She stood up quickly and asked Savanna, her words tinged with urgency, "May I borrow your computer for a minute?" Savanna nodded and they hurried upstairs to Savanna's room.

The adults stood up and stretched, breathing the cool, clear mountain air deeply into their lungs. Christine went inside to freshen their drinks and bring more food. Just as the group had settled again on the deck, talking and laughing, Savanna and Avery rushed back outside. Christine looked closely at her daughter to see if she would give a clue as to what was about to happen, but Savanna just grinned and shook her head slightly. She would never give away the big news that had her mentor trembling with excitement.

Avery motioned for everyone to stay seated. She took center stage and bowed slightly. She lifted her hand and allowed about six or seven pieces of paper to fall gently onto the deck. The wind actually caught one and lifted it in the direction of Brian, who deftly caught it before it could float back down.

Brian glanced at his wife to see her reaction. Christine smiled but shook her head slightly, and looked back at Avery, waiting for her to begin her explanation. Brian sighed, a little too loudly, disappointed that he could not take the lead and "play lawyer." A muffled laugh came from Savanna's direction, but when Brian glanced toward his daughter, her face was the picture of innocence.

Avery waited expectantly for everyone to focus on her. When they were ready, she said, "I know that you are wondering what I went to look up on Savanna's computer." The nods of her audience encouraged her to continue. "Remember when I told you that I had set up a website called 'Miracle Income' and that is how people can sign up to receive the Tokens and give them away?" More nods. "I forgot to tell you that I also set up a Twitter account."

Brian picked up the small piece of paper that had started this entire discussion. "I noticed that," he said as he looked again at the Token. "So the Twitter account is '@MiracleIncome'?"

Avery nodded, glad that someone was familiar with Twitter. Before she could continue, Savanna spoke up, in a voice that only a teenager can muster, "My parents won't let me have a Twitter account." The pained expression on her face as she stole a pleading look at her mom, who immediately said, "NO," caused everyone to laugh.

Avery shook her head in mock disgust at her student's antics before continuing. "I went to see if the Twitter account had any activity." She raised her hands and gestured over the pages lying on the deck, scattered in a haphazard pattern.

Brian took that as his cue to look at the page he had caught earlier. It was a list of tweets from different accounts, all with hashtags that said '#MiracleTokens.' He took a minute to count the number of entries, then announced to the group, "There are 50 tweets on this page alone!"

Avery nodded and smiled. "Look at the date of the first one," she instructed.

Savanna jumped up and started sorting through the papers and finally, she located the earliest date. When the significance of it hit her, she sat down heavily on the deck as if someone had pulled her plug and all the energy had dissolved from her body. Her eyes closed and her face turned toward the sun, a smile flashing across her face. Everyone watched her, wondering what date could have triggered such a reverent reaction.

After several seconds, Savanna opened her eyes and smiled up at her mentor and friend. Love vibrated between them as an almost palpable presence. Avatar woke up from his nap, stretched and walked the few steps to Savanna, sitting quietly in front of her, grinning as only a golden retriever can. Savanna took his face in her hands, and kissed his nose, saying "thank you" to him very softly.

Finally, Savanna stretched out her hand to Avery, who pulled her up into a hug. They turned toward the group and Savanna announced with awe, "The very first tweet was sent on the same day that I met Avery at the park."

Janet Anderson nodded as all of the facts fell into place. She had been quietly watching the interplay between her daughter and Savanna, and now she understood. She stood up and joined the two young women in a group hug.

Christine and Brian still did not appreciate the significance between the two events – when Savanna first met Avery and when the tweets started on the Internet. They looked at each other and shrugged, waiting patiently for an explanation.

Avery could feel their slight frustration and she turned to them and said, "Savanna is my first student after I graduated from the Avalon School. When she accepted me as her teacher, it triggered the Miracle Tokens to begin circulating."

Christine absorbed that information and then made the connection. She stood up and held her hand out to her husband, inviting him to join the circle. He looked at her, puzzlement still written all over his face, but he could not refuse. The strength in her grasp made him study her more closely, but all he could see was joy and love in her eyes.

The last two joined the circle, arms intertwined around waists, swaying gently. Joy and love coursed through them, almost tangible as it connected these people who had just discovered a miracle.

A heart dance.

Avatar raised his head. He had seen this dance many times before, but he never got tired of watching the joy explode on their faces. He jumped up and began barking, the best way that he knew to join the celebration. The sharp sound snapped the moment of reverie and brought everyone back to their physical selves.

Slightly embarrassed and laughing softly, everyone hugged and squeezed each other in recognition and acknowledgment of having witnessed a miracle. They were all slightly breathless and took a minute to regain their sense of selves.

But none of them would ever be the same again. A shift occurred in each heart, which now beat to a new tune of knowing, with absolute certainty, that God was here, right now, loving them while they stood on the deck in the backyard of a home located in Newridge, Colorado. They no longer felt like tiny specs in the cosmos, insignificant and lost. Instead, they mattered...and they were loved beyond their ability to comprehend.

Being seen without their stories to hide behind changed everything.

While the humans gathered themselves and readjusted to their new reality, Avatar started exploring the yard. He soon discovered a tennis ball that was hidden under a pile of leaves. He grabbed it in his large mouth and trotted back to the deck. He walked directly over to Brian, dropping the ball at his feet. Avatar looked up at Brian with a big doggy smile, tail slowly waving back and forth.

Brian laughed and said, "I guess that is as clear an invitation as I will ever get!" He picked up the ball and threw it towards the far end of the yard. Everyone watched mesmerized as Avatar gracefully leap off the deck, and turned towards where the ball was still completing its arc of flight. The moment was suspended in time, and everything went into slow motion.

He actually flew across the yard before he caught the ball!

The moment out of time ended. The women clapped in appreciation but Brian stood at the edge of the deck, stunned by what he had just witnessed. Or did he?

Before Brian could ask the others if they had also seen the dog actually fly, Avatar came panting back, the yellow tennis ball safely encased in his mouth. He dropped it at Brian's feet and sat down, tongue hanging out of the side of his mouth. Brian leaned forward to examine the dog more closely, when the unexpected happened.

Avatar winked.

Brian straightened quickly and turned to the others. "Did you see that?" he cried. "That dog just winked at me!"

To their credit, the four women kept straight faces until Brian turned his back on them. Then they started giggling, heads together and bodies turned inward, sharing a private joke. They were careful not to let Brian hear them, but he sensed something was up. He clearly heard Avery whisper, "He did it again!" and knew that she was referring to her dog.

"Who *are* you?" he asked the dog, squatting down so his face was on the same level as the golden retriever. Brian focused on the physical dog in front of him, while his mind tried to decipher the mystery of what he had just seen. But he forgot about his spiritual self, his soul...that had just surfaced into his awareness.

For an instant, his logical, reasoning mind shut down. And in the span of a heartbeat, he knew the truth. The answer did not come in mere words, but as a subtle acknowledgment of a secret that was about to be revealed.

Liquid brown eyes shining with love stared calmly into Brian's eyes.

Love that was incomprehensible but instantly recognizable by his spiritual self, who leaped in joy.

He was still filled with so much love that he thought he was going to explode. His mind was numb and the usual chattering thoughts were completely absent. In their place was silence, not empty or hollow, but full of love. It almost seemed like a living being, but it was totally still. Complete, in and of itself. Constant but never changing.

He was seen.

And then Avatar winked again, inviting Brian into the dance of the heart.

The End. And the Beginning...

Epilogue

Why are you here, on this planet, at this particular time in history, born into your family with its unique personalities, characteristics and perhaps, dysfunctional relationships? What stories have you created that bring meaning to your experiences, your conflicts, your trials and tribulations? Are there areas in your life where you have stopped growing and evolving?

At some point, every person who has ever taken a breath on this planet has asked these or similar questions.

The book you are holding in your hand (or reading on your screen) contains some of the answers that I discovered as a result of my "wonderings" about my life purpose. *Heart Dancing* is 100%, authentically pure fiction, but no writer can honestly say that she doesn't put a bit of herself into her work.

The same is certainly true for me.

The journey of self-inquiry can begin at any time. For some, tragedy spurs them to ask the tough questions. For others, a failed marriage or a serious health scare can motivate self-awareness. But for me, it was none of those things. I was simply an unfulfilled product of the Baby Boomer Generation. When I turned 48 years old, I reached the sign on my path that read, "Is this all there is?"

Not as dramatic as becoming a widow before the age of 30 or surviving cancer and starting a nonprofit foundation to help raise money for research. But there it is...I was basically dissatisfied with myself and not fulfilled by my chosen career.

The seeds of discontentment can reap a bountiful crop. Once I began to look for answers, it almost seemed as if they were right there in front of me. Of course, that is always true...I had only to open my mind to see them.

Remember to start from where you are and allow your curiosity to lead you forward, one step at a time. You will be amazed at what you discover about yourself, your belief and thought patterns and how they have created your life. Once you have that "Aha" moment, you will recognize that if you created your life as it is today, and then maybe you can create a different life. It is the process of creation at its best --- and your life is the evolving result!

To learn more about these concepts and how to deliberate create your dream life, please visit my website at KathrynEriksen.com. Through my e-course, "Infinite Possibilities: The Art of Joyful Living" to my blog and newsletters, I share valuable information and tools to guide you as you step out in a new direction.

Remember, you are here to reflect God. Be the F.A.C.E. of the Divine and you will learn how to dance with your heart.

My hope for you is that you have started on your own journey towards a spiritual awakening. My dream is that you continue on your path. May the insights contained in this book help guide you, or at least ignite a spark to learn more.

Learn the steps of your own Heart Dance. It's the only way to live!

Blessings, love and light,

Kathryn

Study Guide Questions

Heart Dancing offers some completely radical concepts or ideas. They may be so different from your own beliefs that you reject them as "nonsense," or "unbelievable." That is certainly your prerogative. But if you are reading this part of the book, then you must have made a different decision.

You want to learn more.

One way to do that is to talk about these concepts with others. The following questions might help guide your discussions.

Heart Dancing investigates what happens when the story you have created about an event or situation no longer serves you. Has that ever happened in your life? Did you give up the need to be right? Can you describe how your story prevented you from being seen?

Why do you think that Christine heard the sad music every time she thought about the baby? What purpose did that music serve? Do you think that Christine still hears that same music now that she has begun the healing process?

Discuss how Christine's life changed when she was able to accept the story she created to protect herself from her decision about the baby. She went through a four step process known as Story Alchemy. Step 1 occurred when she realized that she had created a story to support her decision. Step 2 was to take responsibility for her decision and decide to change it. In Step 3, she reframed the events and discovered the lesson that she had avoided by clutching tightly to her story. The final step occurred when Christine released her old story so she could begin to heal.

Are there any stories that you have created about events or people in your life that continue to be painful? What about messages you tell yourself in certain situations that keep you feeling small, unimportant or unloved? To begin the alchemy process, you have to first realize that you have a story or habitual message. Recognition is the first step.

Your thoughts and beliefs create your reality. Do you agree or disagree with that statement? Have you ever experienced the concept of "thoughts become things" in your life?

When you think of your thoughts as packets of energy, does that help you look at them in a more objective way? Name a time when you could have viewed a situation as positive or negative, and explain the decision you made. Then name the thoughts that sprung from that decision. Can you see what a difference it made in your thoughts?

Are you ready to become
the author of your story?

The Story Alchemy Process:

4 Steps to Happiness

If you would like to receive a free summary of The Alchemy Process: 4 Steps to Happiness, please send me an email to info@KathrynEriksen.com. I will gladly share the summary and would love to hear your thoughts and comments about *Heart Dancing*.

To learn more about the Story Alchemy Process and to receive updates, uplifting stories and information, please go to my website at KathrynEriksen.com and sign up with your email address.

Connect With the Author

If your curiosity was piqued by the ideas presented in this book, why not find out more?

Please visit my website at: **www.KathrynEriksen.com**

Facebook: **Facebook/KathrynEEriksen**

Twitter.com: **@KathrynEriksen1** or **@MiracleIncome**

Pinterest.com: **KathrynEriksen**

Miracle Tokens

If the idea of Miracle Tokens captured your imagination, please visit the Miracle Token page on my website and learn how to participate in their distribution.at
www.kathryneriksen.com

To help get you started, on the last page of this book are two Miracle Tokens. Please cut them out and start circulating them. Or send them as a digital message across your social media sites. If you are reading this book as an eBook, please visit my website to receive these Tokens.

Your stories about how you shared Miracle Tokens add to the circulation of spiritual currency. Please add the following to your tweets: #MiracleTokens so we can follow the movement of uplifting energy.

Send me a tweet at @MiracleIncome or @KathrynEriksen1. I would love to connect with you!

Be inspired to share the idea with others. You never know whom you may have touched by your gift.

Heart Dancing is the only way to live!

Sample Miracle Tokens

Please share these Tokens with anyone who needs a smile or a boost. Then tweet about it to let others know that spiritual currency is circulating. Heart Dancing is all about becoming rich in spirit. The fastest way to do that is to give it away!

MIRACLE TOKEN
UNIVERSAL CURRENCY

Smile! You are the face of creation today.

Please add #MiracleToken to your Tweet to let me know
you received this message.   @MiracleIncome

www.MiracleIncome.com

MIRACLE TOKEN

UNIVERSAL CURRENCY

You think that I am the only one who can create? Think again.

Please add #MiracleToken to your Tweet to let me know
you received this message.   @MiracleIncome

www.MiracleIncome.com

18550249R00150

Made in the USA
San Bernardino, CA
19 January 2015